DIRTY DISHES

Recipes To Ignite Passion

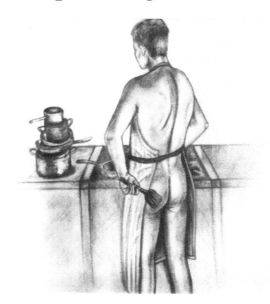

Fiona Lou Collins

Shield  Crest

ISBN: 978-1-913839-35-2

MMXXI

A CIP catalogue record for this
is available from the British Library

Published by
ShieldCrest Publishing Ltd.,
Aylesbury, Buckinghamshire,
HP18 0TF England
Tel: +44 (0) 333 8000 890
www.shieldcrest.co.uk

Dedication

To my ever supportive and encouraging "Mofo" and 'Papa John' for your generosity and non-stop belief. Also to my son and daughter; Luke and Brooke, may I have imparted in you the innate belief that anything is achievable when you set your mind to it!

My loving friends Faro, Claire, Tina and to Bertie, a special thank you to you sir, and long time "bestie", Deja, over in Canada and all those who believed in my vision along the way.

To the people and facilitators of the "make happen" project, thank you Tom, Ollie, Sarah and all the members on the 'screenology' course.

Finally, my thanks to Brooke McNair for the photograph on the front cover and to John Carter, Angela Larry and Lindsey Forrest for the photos in the book.

Foreword

"I first connected with Fiona on social media; I loved her enthusiasm and energy for life.

Conversations with her would brighten anyone's day, no matter how you felt.

All of these traits about Fiona burst through when I read her manuscript for *Dirty Dishes*. I couldn't help but smile at her refreshing, and I must say *risqué* way of engaging her readers. This was definitely Fiona, on a plate.

I was only too delighted to be asked by Fiona to help with many of the "Start You Up" starters, not only because she is a great friend but also because I'm an author, writer and professional chef. I have helped her with the presentation of her other dishes too.

I was literally **blown** away by her knowledge of food and the scientific elements of creating and putting these amazing dishes together, in the book, using various ingredients for her recipes.

This book will put smiles on everyone's faces in all departments, for certain."

PAUL JAMES

Paul is a renowned chef and author of: Great Britain and Cornwall Edition One; Recipes from My Kitchen *and* Recipes from My Travels... New York, New York.

Also creator of worldwide acclaimed social media blogs... Recipes from My Travels; Completely Cornwall *and* Brummagem Rubs & Spices.

Author Comment

I am honoured to collaborate with chef extraordinaire, world traveller and author, Paul James.

I am absolutely convinced that one day he will be SIR Paul James; his dedication, compilation and creation of recipes, indeed, are fit for royalty!

I was fortunate enough to discover Paul's work on social media, almost two years ago, when he was recovering from a life-threatening illness.

I was literally blown away by his mouth-watering dishes, stunning photography and, moreover, the man himself. I admire his humanity and integrity, and his enthusiasm for life inspires many.

Paul has gone from strength to strength in the face of adversity and he is a true inspiration. I am delighted that he has agreed to share with us beautiful souls some of the tastiest and most beautifully presented appetisers we will ever sample. Add to that the bonus of having no jet lag, no queuing, not having to remove half of your clothing, no picking up someone else's bag, no falling out with your partner, nor having to throw away brand-new hair gel. At the time of writing this, we are in lockdown and grounded anyway, but I can remember the ass ache of airports!

Introduction

Firstly, I should issue a warning:

These delectable dishes may incite unbridled passion, and the way to a man's heart, is, apparently, his stomach. Well, that may have some truth but the impetus for this recipe book is to aid in blood flow to the penis. Forget the Viagra, these dishes will bring pleasure to the palate, a tingle on the tongue, plus a whole new flavour in the bedroom. So beware:

If you are taking any medication, especially cholesterol-lowering medication, blood thinners, blood pressure drugs or any other prescribed medication, please check with your physician before using these recipes.

I've been experimenting, in the kitchen... no, not on the *table* but with ingredients. I have conjured and coiffed. Jazzed up in some cases and et voila! My sex life got a whole lot better to boot!

Feed the soul and sexual prowess will follow. Such is my belief and commitment to bring couples together in the way they were intended to be: happy and satisfied, simple.

But who am I, and why am I writing this book? My background is in nursing and having worked on an acute cardiac care unit, I developed an interest in cardiovascular health and general well-being. For as long as I can remember, I have always enjoyed cooking. I learnt that sharing a meal cooked from scratch is a holdall for happiness. My parents weren't so happy with the mess in the kitchen afterwards, but the roast chicken was both edible and quite an achievement for a nine-year-old!

I grew up in an era where health and safety were the domain of hazardous building sites, never featured in the domestic arena.

If something was mouldy or smelled funny, you binned it, or carefully sliced the mould away and ate that bit of cheddar, so a day off school maybe? If you stuck a knife in the toaster and got an electric shock, your mum would say, serves you right, and you NEVER did that again. You get the picture, right?

Many, *many* years ago, plus a few more years later, I found myself single at the age of around forty-eight.

The men I was dating had been freshly clicked from various dating sites; they were of a similar age to me. They often had problems with their nether regions, or in other words, couldn't get it up, and were reliant on the stamina-producing love drug Viagra. As a matter of interest, many of my friends were experiencing the same failures with the men they were intimate with.

All of us ladies felt compassionate I can assure you; it's not pleasant for any man – of whatever generation – to experience this sort of failure. It can make them feel inadequate and depressed, and moreover, unable to sustain a relationship.

I had an epiphany moment one weekend whilst reading a newspaper article on foods that can address Erectile Dysfunction, by aiding blood flow to the male genitalia, as well as boost fertility and sperm motility, liven up flagging libidos and much more. As I've been researching in tandem with my own bespoke recipes, I've found that many of the combinations have the dual impact of lowering cholesterol levels, warding off diabetes, as well as promoting healthy heart function. And lastly, boosting serotonin, having a positive effect on mood and energy.

This was the spring of 2016, and along with the cherry blossoms, an idea was blooming in my mind. The idea was to combine my passion for cooking with my compassion for men at large and, to be honest with you, I do have a strong humanitarian interest. So, I figured just maybe, hopefully, little old me, could actually help other couples in the bedroom department.

So, I took to conducting some research, just to ensure this inkling of mine might be legit, unique and altruistic. I scoured the libraries and scanned the shelves of many bookstores. I found a cornucopia of cookery books: foreign cuisine from every nation; student budget recipes; low-glycaemic-index cookbooks; low-fat recipes, GET fat foods and many more. However, there was not a SINGLE recipe book even remotely addressing the problem of low libido or Erectile Dysfunction.

I wondered: was it too embarrassing to be addressed, or akin to a family secret, like Uncle Bob who had a penchant for wearing women's lingerie on the weekends when he wasn't operating a forklift truck?

I could barely suppress my giggles as I breezed out of one of the Waterstones bookshops. I was onto something, and immediate action had to be taken. This is when my tiny kitchen became a laboratory.

I started cooking up different dishes, using mainly the food groups that were featured in that article I originally read. I added spices, a dash of smoked paprika here, a splash of Tabasco sauce there...

...Chilli, garlic and fragrant herbs like coriander, basil and parsley. The results were a combination of tongue-tantalising recipes; they not only eradicated the need for Viagra but also made my lover feel good, energised and amorous.

Of course, another major thrust – no pun intended – is that the use of Viagra has side effects, like all other drugs. And can be contraindicated with many other drugs such as amlodipine, which is one of the many blood pressure tablets, for example. But before we get cracking, I'd like to alert you to just a few of the side effects of Viagra: upset stomach, abnormal vision, nasal congestion, back pain, nausea, dizziness, rash and diarrhoea, not very sexy, at all. Viagra is also quite expensive and can be hard to obtain. Unlike nutrient-rich and feel-good foods, Viagra is artificial and prone to misuse, just like recreational drugs.

Viagra, or to use the pharmaceutical name, Sildenafil, was originally used to treat hypertension and cardiovascular disease. Researchers found it produced erections in many of its patients. Not so long after this finding, Viagra the love drug was born, so you see, it didn't just pop up! This time, my pun *is*, indeed, intended for your pleasure.

The recipes you will find in this book are all good for you, whether you are male or female. They are low in saturated fats and most of them have slow-release carbohydrates, which helps sustain energy.

Many of the ingredients I use in my recipes have an impact on lowering cholesterol levels. Having high cholesterol levels can lead to atherosclerosis, a condition that clogs and narrows arteries, impairing blood flow. This could lead to heart problems that usually manifest below the belt, to begin with. The arteries surrounding the genital area are narrower than coronary blood vessels and therefore, more susceptible to clots. In a nutshell, the better your cholesterol level, the better your erection will be as well.

Before you get all hot and bothered, slaving in the kitchen, I have shortlisted the fruits, vegetables, herbs, spices, and beverages, that sing their sonata of libido-boosting benefits. For simplicity, and at a glance, engagement, I am going for the magic number of three, in each category. There is a cornucopia of edibles that can relight your desire, but why waste time agonising over laborious lists, when instead, you can be kissing each other's lips?

Foods That Put Oomph into Your Love Life

Let's start getting all fruity. (NB: Erectile Dysfunction – ED)

FRUITS

Bananas – The *Men's Health* magazine compiled a list of foods to "keep the pecker up" – Bananas were included, mostly for high levels of potassium, which is excellent for the heart, circulation and helps to keep blood pressure in check. Their shape, is undeniably phallic, a little hint from nature?

Blueberries – say goodbye to "blue balls"! These rotund purple pleasures contain one of the six flavonoids, influencing ED. Anthocyanins in the blueberry are associated with a reduced risk of the floppy disk. Delicious and so good for you, they are high in antioxidant properties too.

Figs – No need to hide your dignity with these biblical delights. Figs contain magnesium, a mineral essential to the production of sex hormones, like androgen and oestrogen, which have some control over your libido. Figs also contain an amino acid that increases the production of nitric oxide, important for expanding the blood vessels and increasing the flow below.

HERBS

Basil – This heady scented herb will leave you swooning. Apparently, the Ancient Greeks fed it to their stallions prior to being bred. Perhaps it's the sweet scent of basil that causes sexual desire? At any rate, this herb is a winner at the gate; it's readily available and can be used on just about anything, from salads to soups to hot pots.

Coriander – Pretty, fragrant and easy to use, coriander also helps aid digestion. This herb was popular in ancient societies. Believing it to be so sacred, the Egyptians placed it into the pharaohs' tombs to bring them whoopee on the other side. It may protect the heart by lowering LDL cholesterol and blood pressure. The seeds help women feel sexy.

Rosemary – A herb with a beautiful and intense aroma, it has a stimulating effect on the senses and helps improve memory. Rosemary has a long history as an aphrodisiac as well as being multi-medicinal. It is easily cultivated in the kitchen and replanted in the garden or on a balcony. This is a herb that packs a powerful punch when it comes to good health. Usage is simple, you can bake with it, pierce it into meat, cheese or add to soups and stews. So effective.

SPICES

Cloves – Warming clove invites flavour. The scent is said to improve sexual behaviour and boost energy. Cloves are versatile to use in pumpkin pie or mulled chai tea, cider or wines.

Ginger – An aphrodisiac in many cultures, it is a great libido booster. It especially helps to increase blood flow to the loins. Ginger can help your energy levels and is high in potassium, magnesium and copper. Add to a morning smoothie for an energy boost or drink it as a tea.

Saffron – Only a tiny amount of this stuff is necessary, a little will go a long way. It helps increase both sex drive and sex function. It boasts high antioxidant properties and supplies selenium, zinc, potassium and magnesium, making it a super mood booster. Try it with potatoes or rice.

VEGETABLES

Celery – Surprisingly, yes, it *is* an aphrodisiac; certainly, it is appropriately shaped. During the Renaissance period, celery was a delicacy for Louis XV, allegedly prepared by his mistress to maintain his energy for mounting her. Too mythological? More modern-day findings are that celery can increase the pheromone called androsterone; also, it contains chemicals that can help dilate blood vessels, increase sex drive as well as heighten climax. Delicious with a Caesar cocktail or in a glass of seasoned tomato juice.

Asparagus – Although it can make your pee smell a bit whiffy, these stalks contain plenty of folate and vitamin B6, which can boost orgasm and arousal.

Pumpkin – These and their seeds are extremely rich in zinc and promote prostate gland health. Zinc is instrumental to sex drive and a great libido booster, rich in Omega-3, pumpkins are beneficial for heart protection. Often the first sign of a heart problem is manifest in the inability to gain an erection.

BEVERAGES

Red wine – Goes to your head, or so they sang, they were not wrong! A rich antioxidant profile in the red elixir triggers nitric oxide production in the blood. This relaxes artery walls, increasing blood flow to the other head!

Pomegranate juice – The oh, so juicy, "pom" is a veritable love potion, when juiced. According to *The International Journal of Impotence*, research, found that it had a positive effect on erectile dysfunction, due to powerful antioxidants that support blood flow. These glistening little jewels can turn a salad sexy, scattered on top. Speaking of on top... you will be!

Coffee – It's no wonder coffee parlours have been popping up all over the place in the UK and seem to be heaving with couples sipping together. According to male fertility online (www.malefertilityonline.com), coffee may be the biggest libido booster around. They claim it has been shown (in animal studies) to put the females in a rampant mood. Get grinding those coffee beans and you'll be ready to espresso yourself in no time!

A FEW MORE JUST FOR FUN

Red meat - Burger or sirloin steak, iron laden red meat of all varieties, can assist with fatigue, irritability and just plain old tiredness, which is not good for a round of sexual aerobics, or even energy saving, missionary position! Honey, it's steak night!

Nuts - Do not dare me on the subject. Seriously though, love-makers, pistachios, peanuts and walnuts all contain the amino acid, L-arginine. I am no professor, but I *have* done my research to ensure you're getting the best information. Go crazy for your nuts as they help with cholesterol levels, which is good news for blood flow.

Oatmeal - No wonder they say "get your oats"! The popular breakfast grain is also a good source of L-arginine, an amino acid commonly used to treat erectile dysfunction. Also, grains like oatmeal are beneficial in controlling cholesterol levels.

Oysters - These overtly sexual sea creatures have one of the highest concentrations of zinc, a mineral associated with semen production and found in healthy semen. Research reveals that oysters contain two unusual amino acids, D-aspartic d and N-methyl-aspartate. Researchers from Barry University in Miami found that these amino acids increase sex hormones in rats.

Chillies - Are excellent to bring out the flavour in a dish and also add a burst of colour. The health benefits are plentiful, aiding digestion and promoting healthy heart function. Often the first sign of a heart problem is not being able to achieve or maintain an erection. Chillies can lower blood serum cholesterol and reduce lipid deposits, and so, reverse excessive blood clotting. The effect of chillies on blood vessels is dilation, which will help you get the rise you desire.

Panax Ginseng, Maca, Ginkgo and Ginger – These herbs and spices can all be beneficial for increasing sex drive and aiding in ED. All of these can be taken as supplements that you can find in most health food shops. I go to Holland & Barratt, the staff there are friendly and knowledgeable.

Pumpkin Seeds, Chia Seeds & Sesame Seeds - Like oysters, pumpkin seeds are extremely rich in zinc and promote prostate gland health. Zinc is instrumental to sex drive and a great libido booster. Rich in Omega-3, it is beneficial for heart protection. Chia seeds contain high levels of magnesium, which helps your cells release energy, good for a round of sexual aerobics. Sesame seeds contain lignin, which helps sperm count and quality.

Contents

START YOU UPS

GET DOWN TO ITS

SWEET NOTHINGS

Popeye oh, Popeye – Olive

Black-eyed Beans & Sautéed Garlic-Infused Spinach

Popeye's Passion

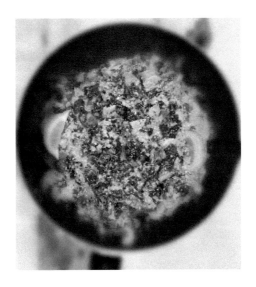

Olives everywhere will love their "Popeyes" after trying this sensational dish, devised by the fabulous chef, Paul James. Spinach is a folate-rich food, which is essential for those muscles, um, popping up. One cup of cooked spinach contains a whopping 65 per cent of your daily folic acid intake.

I can't help but think of the classic cartoon; now we *know* why he was winking with just the one eye! This wonder green contains the all-essential blood-pumping mineral, magnesium, which, along with helping heart health, assists hard-on health too, as it helps to boost testosterone levels. Black-eyed beans contain many of the

1

B vitamins and iron, which boost endorphins, the happy hormones that can increase your sex drive.

What to do it with:

1 tbsp vegetable oil
Mustard seeds
Fenugreek seeds
Dried red chillies or chilli powder
1 garlic clove
6 fresh curry leaves
Baby spinach
1 tsp ground coriander
1 tsp ground cumin
400g can black-eyed beans
200g can tinned tomatoes
Peanuts
Jasmine rice

How to do it:

In a hot frying pan, add a tbsp of oil. Add mustard seeds, fenugreek seeds, dried chilli flakes. Cook gently until the mustard seeds pop.
Add the curry leaves and garlic and gently cook until the garlic is just starting to go slightly golden.
Add the cumin and coriander powder, and gently cook for a couple of minutes.
Add 100 grams of tinned tomatoes and 200 grams of black-eyed beans.
Then a handful of baby spinach. Cook until the spinach has wilted.

Leave to go cold and then blitz in a blender, season to taste and return to a small saucepan and gently warm through.

Clean out your frying pan, add some more very thin slivers of garlic, sea salt and the rest of the black-eyed beans.
Take a handful of spinach, a tablespoon of water and cook until wilted.
Present on a warm plate with Thai Jasmine rice, peanuts and the delicately spiced purée.

'All you need is love. But a little chocolate now and then doesn't hurt.'

Charles M Schultz

Beetroot with Celeriac & Honey Soup

"My Heart skips a Beet"

Beetroot, with its vibrant pink stain, can do wonders for your sexual health. For one thing, it's high in nitric oxide, which helps dilate blood vessels and increase that all essential blood flow. Turnip-rooted vegetable or Knob celery are other names for celeriac... knob celery, I *had* to say it again, is great for bone health—I kid you not. It's also a plentiful source of vitamin K. All innuendo aside, celeriac really can help reduce the risk of fractures. It is also rich in vitamin C, raising the levels of ascorbic acid in plasma, which reduces the risk of high blood pressure, associated with cardiovascular disease and stroke.

Honey now, rich in the B vitamin group, which is needed for making testosterone which I call the humping hormone. The fructose in honey offers a nice, slow and steady release of energy, resulting in your increased stamina.

What to do it with:

2 tbsp olive oil
2 tbsp of salted butter
2 small onions, diced
2 cloves garlic, minced or chopped
1 pack 200g pre-cooked beetroot, cubed
400g celeriac, peeled and cubed
3 cm fresh ginger, peeled and chopped
Juice of 1 small lemon
2 tbsp honey
1 litre of vegetable or chicken stock
30g toasted hazelnut or walnut
1-2 tbsp sour cream
Chilli flakes & parsley leaves to garnish

How to do it:

Over medium heat, warm the olive oil first before adding the butter and fry the onion for 5 minutes, before adding the garlic. Fry for a further 2 minutes.

Rinse the beetroot thoroughly to remove the vinegar taste, throw it in with the celeriac, giving it all a right good stir.

Now in with the ginger, lemon juice and honey, taste for balance. If you wish, you can add more honey, it's all about personal taste. Incorporate the stock you are using and once again stir it all nicely in. Slowly bring to the boil and reduce to a simmer. Cover for about 30 minutes, checking at the 20-minute mark to make sure the vegetables are becoming nice and tender.

Whilst all this is going on, take a small frying pan and heat the base up, just a little, before toasting the walnuts or hazelnuts. Do this until they are slightly charred and releasing their sweet odour, around 3 minutes.

Once the soup is cooked, remove it from the heat and with a handheld blender, purée the soup until you get the desired consistency; you may need to add a little more stock.

Serve immediately with the sour cream, nut topping, chilli flakes and parsley, if using.

'Hard work should be rewarded by good food.'

Ken Follet

Stuffed Peppers with Quinoa, Feta and Toasted Hazelnuts

"Quinoa you"

Once again, this delectable, delicious starter or main that's also good for you is simple to make and looks impressive. Quinoa ticks a *lot* of boxes: it's gluten-free, high in protein and boasts a high antioxidant profile. Quinoa was grown in the Inca empire, dubbed the mother of all grains and thought to be sacred. Red peppers, in particular, contain lycopene which is great for heart health plus vitamins A and C, which have powerful antioxidant qualities. Artery-health-improving hazelnuts have a high concentration of healthy fats and help to lower blood cholesterol.

These ingredients combined help to clear the way for healthy blood flow, to where it's most required and your heart too (see next page for homemade tomato ragu).

7

What to do it with:

2 red peppers (or for aesthetics, use 1 orange pepper)
200g quinoa
100g crumbled feta
50g toasted crushed hazelnuts
50g grated parmesan
50g butter to melt into quinoa
Homemade baked tomato ragu (optional)

How to do it:

Set the oven for 200°C. Prepare the quinoa according to packet instructions.
In a small dry frying pan toast the hazelnuts, about 4 minutes; add a little salt to bring out the flavour.
Core and deseed the peppers, retaining the tops intact. Once the quinoa is cooked, fluff it up with a fork.

Add the butter into the quinoa. Allow it to melt so it's nice and moist. Tip in the crumbled feta and parmesan, then the nuts and give it all a good stir.

Stand the peppers in a Pyrex or similar dish and fill with the quinoa mix and put the "lids" on.

Bake in the oven for 30 minutes or until slightly browned.

Serve immediately with the ragu or enjoy on their own.

'I beg your pardon, I never promised you a rose garden.'

Barry Harris

A Simple Tomato Ragu or Sauce

"You saucy thing"

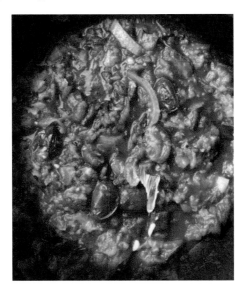

As promised, I give you the sauce. This sumptuous ragu is so versatile, it can be used as a base for Bolognese and soups or enjoyed on its own or over a hot potato, but indeed, and please do, pour over the stuffed peppers from the previous page. I have adapted this recipe from that created by the most admirable chef, the amazing Marco Pierre White. The sexiness is in its simplicity, and the taste so divine, you can offer it up to your goddess, or god. You are worthy!

What to do it with:

Olive oil
1 white or red onion, finely chopped or grated
2 cloves of minced or chopped garlic
300g cherry tomatoes, halved

9

1 can good quality chopped tomatoes
150 ml vegetable or chicken stock
2 sprigs of thyme
2 Bay leaves
Salt and pepper to season

How to do it:

Over medium heat, drizzle the olive oil into a pan, add the onions and garlic and cook till they're soft, about 4 minutes.
Add in the cherry tomato halves and cook until slightly broken down to release their sweet juices.
Add the chopped tomatoes and the stock. Give it all a nice stir, then in with the thyme and bay leaves. Bring it all to a purring boil, then lower the heat for 20 minutes.
Remove from heat, give it a good stirring and place into an oven-proof covered dish and bake for a further 20 minutes on 150 C. Allow to sit for 10 minutes and then pour over your peppers on the plates of love!

'The day ain't nuthin' till you've had a muffin'

(Seen in a café window in Texas)

Bacon, Tomato and Cheese Muffins

"Cheese, you're cute"

These Buckwheat Breakfast Bites will set you up nicely till well beyond lunchtime. Let me talk tomatoes with you, these amazing plums have many health benefits for men. They can help to increase fertility by improving the shape of the male sperm; the little "swimmers" developed a superior stroke in studies where men's intake of tomatoes was increased compared to the men who ate none or little of this red produce. Red fruits and vegetables, such as tomatoes, watermelon and strawberries, contain lycopene, an antioxidant that can have beneficial effects on the body, this includes your todger health too! Blood flow to the penis is improved which can give men stronger erections. Start growing your own; tomatoes are extremely easy to grow and harvest. According to gardenersworld.com, some varieties of tomato are well-suited to growing in hanging baskets, perfect for small gardens or balconies. So now you can be well hung outdoors too!

What to do it with:

Splash of olive oil or as much as you like
6-8 plum tomatoes off the vine
4 rinds of bacon (smoked or unsmoked)
4 rounds of chopped chorizo
130g buckwheat flour
½ tbsp baking powder
1 free-range egg
120 ml milk or soya milk
1 tbsp melted butter
50g grated cheese (your preference)
Pinch of Italian mixed dried herbs

How to do it:

Preheat oven to 180°C. Pop 6 muffin cases into a muffin tray. Heat a frying pan with olive oil and add the bacon. Once that has started to cook, add the plum tomatoes and chorizo. Fry till bacon is to your liking and set aside.

In a mixing bowl, sieve the flour and add baking powder. Put the butter in a pan to melt while you beat the egg.

Make a well in the dried mixture, add the wet ingredients and stir in or use an electric beater, just make sure you get a nice stiff batter. Add the bacon mixture, chopped chorizo and cheese, stir in gently to incorporate thoroughly.

Using a tablespoon, or ice-cream scoop, put 2 scoops or tablespoons in each muffin case.

Place in the hot oven and bake for 25-30 minutes or until golden brown.

Allow them to cool slightly before biting into them. The muffins will keep in the fridge for 3 days or can be frozen for up to a week.

'Life is like a giant hors d'oeuvre tray in that it is to be savored.'

Jack Fitzgerald

Gnocchi with Chilli, Basil, Parsley and Garlic Butter

"Having nooky with gnocchi tonight"

This wonderful recipe from author and chef, Paul James, in his book *Recipes from My Travels.* It's delicious and fairly easy to prepare, just needs a little patience. Potatoes are the jewels of the earth, so claims Marco Pierre White. He is quite right, as the unassuming root vegetable has cosied its way to rub up against the superfoods, due to its high levels of vitamin C, B6, folate, magnesium and potassium. Potatoes also help to keep blood sugar levels in check and can help prevent heart disease. Parsley packs a powerful punch, in that it builds female libido by encouraging hormones and neurotransmitters conducive to arousal and satisfaction response. It also helps to combat garlic breath, but you knew that anyway, right? Garlic, as you've heard me say, is excellent for boosting both the immune system and sex drive. It contains a compound that increases blood flow to male *and* female sex organs.

What to do it with:

The saucy:
1 large clove of garlic, finely sliced
1 red chilli, finely sliced
Fresh basil, finely sliced
100g of butter

The Gnocchi
3 large potatoes (King Edward or Maris Piper)
70g flour
1 medium free-range egg
Salt & pepper
Peel and cut the potatoes into chunks, then place them in a saucepan with the salt. Cover with cold water and bring to the boil. Cover and simmer until cooked.
Drain and set aside for 10 minutes without a lid on to let them dry out.
Add salt & pepper to taste then mash the potatoes until you have no lumps.
Sift the flour into the potatoes and mix while slowly adding the egg to make a thick dough.
Set aside for 10 minutes to allow the mixture to cool slightly.
With floured hands, roll the dough into sausage shapes, then cut into 1-inch pieces.
Roll the gnocchi with the back of a fork to create ridges.

REFRIGERATE FOR AN HOUR

Bring a pan of slightly salted water to the boil.
When ready, add the gnocchi to the saucepan of water.

Once the gnocchi starts to float to the top of the pan, it's cooked. Drain well.

The Saucy bit:

In a frying pan, add the butter to it along with the garlic and chilli. Fry on high heat for about 30 seconds to a minute. Make sure the garlic does not burn.
Add the gnocchi and fry gently until golden brown.
Add the parsley and basil and serve straight away.

'If food be the love of life, spread me a banquet.'

My inner Shakespeare

Scallops with a Black Pudding Crumb

"You make me crumb"

Scallops could be dance partner to the oyster, robustly bursting with zinc and a raging reputation as aphrodisiacs. This pearl of the sea, the silky, sexy scallop is described thus by no accident, as they contain compounds that help men and women feel amorous.

Black pudding has been categorised as a superfood; oh, I know! It is rich in iron and protein, all good for energy levels and a rampant session requires that kind of energy! This recipe is mouth-watering and super simple to prepare.

What to do it with:

110g scallops (Cornish, if available)
25g black pudding

Cucumber
Fennel
Handful of cooked peas
Apple sauce
Juice of half a lemon
Knob of butter
Pea shoots and pomegranate seeds to garnish
Sea salt

How to do it:

Crumble the black pudding into a hot dry pan and cook until crisp. Heat a medium-sized pan until it's smoking and drizzle in a bit of olive oil. Place your scallops gently into the pan and cook for about 2-3 minutes without shaking or moving them. Turn gently over and season with a bit of salt, lemon juice and your knob of butter.
Continue to baste the scallops with the butter until they are nicely seared, beautifully opaque in colour and cooked. Leave to drain for a few moments on kitchen paper.

Assemble your salad firstly by cutting the fennel in half and slice thinly but CAREFULLY with a mandarin, repeat the same with the cucumber.

Place your scallops on the top of the salad. Then, put some of the black pudding crumb on top and decorate the dish with pea shoots, peas and pomegranate seeds and apple sauce purée. Drizzle some of the juices from the pan over the scallops and enjoy.

'Food is like sex, when you abstain, even the worst stuff, begins to look good.'

Beth McAllister

Anise-Steamed Cod with Lemongrass and Pea Purée

"Tease me peas me"

This is another mouth-tingling wonder from the renowned Paul James. Fish, as you've heard me rave about, is a key food when it comes to steaming up windows! Sex educator and author, Dr Yvonne Kristin Fulbright, touted the benefits of Omega-3 fish oil in a FOX News article, entitled, "Can You Eat Your Way to Better Sex?" (2005). The essential Omega-3 benefits of this steamed cod dish are more prevalent than in a fried or deep-fried cod meal, as it seems the frying process eradicates the Omega-3.

In *The Orgasmic Diet*, a book by consultant Marrena Lindberg, taking ample amounts of fish oil and following a diet low in carbohydrates can help women enjoy heightened orgasms and boost their sex lives.

What to do it with:

1 cod fillet (no skin)
300g frozen peas
2 Lemongrass stalks
Anise syrup (alcohol-free) or a small glass of Pernod
Salt & pepper to taste
100ml of milk or water (for the pea purée)

How to do it:

Take two small saucepans and fill them both with 300 ml water. In the first saucepan, place the peas and lemongrass (slightly crushed). Cover and rapidly boil for 10 minutes. Turn off the heat and leave it to sit in the covered pan.

In the next saucepan, add the Anise syrup to the water and bring to a boil. Place the cod fillet in a steamer or colander and allow the anise mixture to rapidly boil.

After 6 minutes, turn off the heat and let the cod take in the aniseed flavour. Drain the peas and remove the lemongrass stalks. Put the peas in a blender and add a drop of milk to loosen. Sieve into a clean pan, season to taste and gently heat. Put the flaked cod on top of the pea purée.

'After a good dinner, one can forgive anybody, even one's own relatives.'

Oscar Wilde

A Steak Marinade

"Marinade in Heaven"

This great marinade I conjured is simply a taste sensation! Fireworks will go off in your mouth, exploding you and your love partner into sheer ecstasy. All of the ingredients carefully combined, are a concoction of powerful particles, to ensure a lift in libido and energy. Apple Cider Vinegar (ACD), though not directly related to ED, *does* help the causes of "limber timber". Just taking 2 tbsp of ACD each morning, straight up, or in your OJ, can have a deep impact on lowering cholesterol levels, blood lipid levels and blood sugar levels, all of which contribute to heart disease. Remember one of the first signs of heart problems is that "sleepy wood"! There are two ways you can have this as a luxurious starter, the first is to marinade for 2 hours and then pan fry. The second is to sear the steaks and slow cook for 8 hours, so the steak melts in the mouth. The choice, darlings, is yours.

What to do it with:

2 sirloin or rump steaks
1 tbsp tomato purée
2 tsp garlic purée
2 tsp dark & rich runny honey
1 tsp garlic salt granules
2 tsp crushed dried chillies
1 tsp ground black pepper
1 tbsp Heinz ketchup
2 tsp apple cider vinegar
1 tsp red wine vinegar
1 tbsp dried
1 chopped fresh chilli
2 tsp fresh ginger
1-2 tsp smoked paprika
½ tsp fish sauce
1 tbsp apricot jam
1 tsp soya sauce
1 tsp wholegrain

How to do it:

This is all about working it *slowly* and incorporating gradually, tasting all the way through this combining process.

In a bowl do the following (or if you are going the slow cooker option, go directly into the slow cooker pot, turned off till your steaks are ready to whack in there).

Beginning with the tomato and garlic purée, stirring with wood, I mean, a wooden spoon, in with the honey, honey.

Around the time you've incorporated the fish sauce, begin to finger dip for taste, you can add more of the remaining ingredients. If apricot jam is not to your liking, you can use a different kind of jam or omit it completely.

Steep your meat or marinade for 2 hours at least, or overnight if you really want to taste the sweet juices of this marinade in heaven.

'Great food is like great sex. The more you have the more you want.'

Gael Greene

Avocado Stuffed with Smoked Haddock

"You're everything avo wanted"

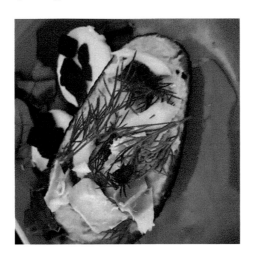

This awesome appetiser is not just delicious on the lips, the richness of potassium and vitamin B-6 contained in the avocado, livens up libido too. Lianne Young, a qualified nutritionist, says they're great for boosting your sex life; she claims they raise the energy levels vital for sex drive and help your man last longer. Whilst smoked haddock is not specified as testosterone-charged, it is claimed that all fish, being rich in protein and zinc, improves sperm motility and testosterone synthesis. According to the *Global Journal of Health Science*, regular consumption of fish and seafood helps lower the risk of heart disease, lowers the risk of diabetes and dementia and helps protect against cancer. This recipe is adapted from Marco Pierre White's course on 'BBC Maestro'.

What to do it with:

2 large ripe avocado pears
1 half lemon to squeeze
A splash of olive oil
Sea salt crystals
Black pepper
1 large fillet of smoked haddock (cook in the bag from Morrison's)
A few sprigs of thyme
2 chives spliced in 3

How to do it:
Cook the fish in the microwave as per packet instructions—usually 2 minutes. Discard skin and flake flesh into a bowl. Set aside.

Lop the bottoms off each avocado so that they can stand on a plate. Gently peel away the skin and then ever so carefully slice round the avocado and twist the top bit off. With a paring knife, dig into the stone and with a gentle twist, remove it.

Into the cavity, put the smoked haddock; add a little lemon juice and seasoning. Only fill the cavity and replace the top half. The rest of the haddock can be spooned delicately onto the serving plates.

With a tiny bit of olive oil, brush the avocado and, using light fingers, adhere a few sprigs of the thyme. Then, on each half of the pear, add the spliced chive, to give the dish that Michelin-star aesthetic. Finish with a sprinkle of salt crystals and splashes of olive oil on the plates

'Age and glasses of wine should never be counted'

Anon.

A Lamb Phaal

"Phaal at your Feet"

The main reason for concocting and adapting this sumptuous lamb phaal was to impress my current lover and to challenge myself, in tandem. Not only was he impressed with the final result, but I, too, was impressed with his stamina, long after dinner. Chillies are a great circulation booster, with peripheral powers in aiding digestion. Chillies pump up immunity, warding off unsexy infections.

Ancient Chinese people believed that coriander could give them mortality; the Egyptians accorded the herb such honour that it was placed in the tombs of pharaohs, believing it would bring great sex on the other side. Coriander is also good for aiding digestion and its oils are mood-enhancing—a dish, then, to inspire good mood and great sex, certainly a winning combo.

What to do it with:

3 tbsp vegetable or olive oil
500g diced lamb
1 onion finely chopped
4 tsp ginger purée
9 cloves garlic finely chopped
1 tsp ground cumin
1 tsp turmeric
3 tsp curry powder
2 tsp garam masala
1 tsp hot paprika
4 tbsp dried chillies
1 400g tin chopped tomatoes
200ml chicken stock
Salt and ground black pepper to season
Coriander to garnish

How to do it:

Heat oil in a large wok over high heat until sizzling. Add lamb in batches until nicely browned on all sides, roughly 8 minutes; reduce heat if oil begins to smoke.

Repeat with the second batch of the lamb. Remove the lamb and add the onion to the hot oil. Cook until translucent, about 4 minutes.

Add the ginger and garlic, stirring in until fragrant, about 3 minutes. Add cumin, turmeric, curry powder, garam masala and hot paprika.

Cook until the spices are fragrant and take on a nutty aroma, about 4 minutes. Add chilli flakes and stir to combine. Return the lamb and coat gently with the spice mixture.

Pour in the chopped tomatoes and chicken stock over high heat and reduce as soon as it all begins to bubble up.

Simmer for one and a half hours, stirring occasionally. Once the lamb is tender and sauce is reduced, season with salt and pepper. Serve with brown basmati rice or new potatoes with crushed cumin seeds, but this is optional.

'People who love to eat are always the best people.'

J. Child

A Lamb Tagine

"Zesty Beast"

I reckon this one would definitely keep Ray Winstone (star of 'Sexy Beast') up for the night, and I don't mean stargazing either. With the chilli and orange zest in this daring dish, it will be bursting with flavour... ooh, I am tingling already! Now then, save the calamari for later, "babe". To keep with tradition, I've cooked this lovely jubbly in a tagine. Chilli peppers boast a bevvy of health benefits, they boost the immune system, help alleviate joint pain and much more. Of the most relevant benefit for ED, they are a natural way to support cardiovascular function and prevent heart disease. These little treasures can get your blood pumping to *that* nether region. Oranges are brimming with vitamin C, as we all know! According to a study by US and Canadian researchers, a class of compounds found in the citrus fruit peels, called Polyethoxylated Flavones (PMFs) have the potential to lower cholesterol more effectively than some prescription drugs. Oranges help keep blood pressure under check as they are high in B6, a vitamin that supports the production of haemoglobin. A *Journal of Sexual Medicine* study revealed that red wine has a rich antioxidant profile that triggers nitric oxide production in the blood, which in turn relaxes artery walls, causing the blood to flow with more ease to those nether regions. It's all about chemistry!

What to do it with:

300g stewing steak or beef, cubed
3 tbsp olive oil
2 large red onions, chopped
1 beef cube
400ml water to dissolve
Dijon mustard
1 cm grated ginger
3 cloves of garlic
100 ml red wine
3 small oranges, juice and zest
1 star anise
1 tsp coriander, dried
1 tsp cumin, dried
1 tsp nutmeg
1 tsp paprika
1 red chilli, whole
1 green chilli, whole
1 lime leaf
200ml passata
200g button mushrooms

How to do it:

Place the meat in a sufficiently sized bowl, and, with clean hands, lovingly mix the spices together and rub them right into that succulent meat.

Heat half the oil in a large pan or wok and brown the onions and place in your tagine, then brown the meat in the remaining hot oil—this should be done in batches to get meat nicely browned. Transfer it all to the tagine and add all your remaining ingredients, except the mushrooms, which you will want to put in for the final half-hour.

Bring to a gentle boil, then reduce heat and simmer for two and a half hours.

Serve with couscous or rice.

'Food is symbolic of love when words are inadequate.'

Alan D. Wolfelt

A Steak Stir-fry

"Stir me up"

This very quick and easy meal will have you both shaking at the knees; it's both delectable and delicious with a hint of Eastern persuasion. So quick, you won't have time to unzip each other.

The Thai-style grains are good for energy and are easily digested. The quinoa helps to lower cholesterol levels which helps to reduce fatty deposits in the blood, lowering the risk of heart disease. Again, the ginger, which I have alerted you to before, can assist with a plethora of ailments, including arthritis. Finally, the steak has iron, in Arnold Schwarzenegger doses, increasing energy levels, to the "I'll be back" status!

This very humble dish is a delight and so simple, Arnie could make it! (Sorry, Arnie, please don't beat me up.)

What to do it with:

2 frying steaks, using any oil
1 inch ginger, grated
1 tbsp garlic paste
1 tbsp chilli paste
1 500g bag Thai stir fry or any other
250g Brussels sprouts
3 tbsp sesame oil
1 or 2 pouches Thai-style grains or rice
2 tsp sesame seeds

How to do it:

Get a griddle pan nice and hot and slap your steaks down; 3 minutes each side for rare, longer if you prefer well-done steaks.

Whilst the steak is cooking, splash some sesame stir fry oil in a wok or frying pan and do your veggies and ginger until al dente. After that, set aside in a separate dish and keep warm in the oven, or you can always zap in the microwave to reheat.

To the still-hot stir-fry pan, add the sprouts and cook with the garlic and chilli pastes, about 10 minutes till they look charred and tender. Incorporate the steak; I use scissors to cut mine into strips, but you can do whatever you prefer. The great thing about my recipes is you can make them your own, play around with them to suit your taste, adding more spice or seasoning.

Once you get to blending all the veg with the steak, heat the bag of grains or rice, or even noodles and simply add to the main attraction, stirring it all up, or in! Dish out into bowls and sprinkle with the sesame seeds.

'There is no sincerer love than the love of food.'

G.B. Shaw

Erotic Ocean Pie with Sweet Potato Mash

"Deep-sea jiving"

Under the sea, and under the sheets right after, this quick and simple dish will guarantee you both going for a big splash after, no skinny dipping required. All fish contain healthy amounts of iodine which is essential for thyroid function; in turn, this gland being well oiled gives rise to energy being released. We are all aware that lovemaking burns a lot of calories. Ocarina, yam or sweet potato all boast antioxidant properties, and these orange spuds get their rich colour from beta carotene. They are rich in vitamin C as well as A, which boosts fertility and energy-giving iron. Marvellous mustard seeds have health benefits as long as a lazy Sunday. Most significantly, they are instrumental in sexual dysfunction. These, "super" seeds contain high levels of vitamins and minerals which aid in lowering blood pressure and preventing atherosclerosis (hardening of the arteries). We only want to achieve a good, healthy hard-on!

What to do it with:

500g seafood mixture OR 2 salmon fillets and 6-8 tiger prawns
50g butter
The juice of half a lemon
4 peeled and chopped sweet potatoes
1 tsp nigella seeds
1 tsp mustard seeds
1 tsp smoked paprika
A handful of parmesan flakes or any other grated cheese, or both
1 sprig of parsley to dress

How to do it:

Preheat your oven to 180°C
First of all, you will want to put your sweet spuds on the hob to boil till soft enough to make a fluffy mash, roughly 25 minutes.

Prepare your fish ingredients with butter and lemon juice and season with salt and pepper. Wrap in foil and bake in the oven for 20 minutes on 180°C

Once cooked, transfer the fish or seafood mixture to a lasagne dish, you will want to have a dish that is at least 2 or more inches deep.

Drain the sweet potatoes and reserve a little of the liquid from their pan, about 100 ml. Once drained, mash them up to a fluffy crescendo, add a splash of milk and a nice knob of butter. Add the nigella and mustard seeds. I like to dry roast my mustard seeds just till they pop and toast, to release their flavour. Spread evenly over your fish mixture with a sprinkle of paprika and the parmesan flakes, place under a medium grill till browned and slightly crispy.

'Success is a tasty dish. Patience, intelligence, knowledge and experience are its 'ingredients'. But, 'hard work' is that little salt that makes it 'Delicious'.'

Anon.

Chickpea & Butternut Squash Stew

"Sexy Chick"

This sexy, heart-warming, blood-pumping dish is delightful for those chilly winter nights. The crowning glory is the coriander. It is well known throughout Asia as a powerful and long-lasting aphrodisiac - phwoar! Also, garlic not only protects the heart but gives the circulation a good pumping. Garlic lowers cholesterol levels which means clearer arteries for a more easy flow to those naughty, nether regions. Cook together for the tasting trial process; it's nice to spoon a bit into each other's hungry mouths, open wide sugar lips!

What to do it with:

1 butternut squash
2 tsp dried coriander
1 tsp cumin seeds

50g butter
Splash of olive oil
2 cloves garlic
1 red onion chopped
1 can chopped tomatoes
2 tsp brown sugar
3 tbsp tomato purée (use a garlic one for more flavour)
1 can chickpeas
1 red or green chilli (red looks lush)
Fresh coriander to garnish
150g tub of crème fraiche

How to do it:

Preheat oven to 200°C and simply pop in the whole squash. Bake for 1 hour and allow to cool. Pour a hot bath, with seductive soaps and blow bubbles together for that hour if you so wish?

Or, simply stay in the kitchen with a bottle of "bubbly"... the choice is yours, my lovers.

Dry fry the spices for just a few minutes and set aside. Heat a pan till fairly hot and add the butter with the oil and sizzle your onion and garlic till just nicely browning and chuck in the brown sugar. Add the tomatoes and tomato paste. Stir gently, then add your spices.
Now the sampling, more spice? Up to you two tasty tasters. To this mix add your chickpeas. Remove the squash from the oven and allow a good half hour to cool. Once it has, slice in half and scoop out the seeds. Cube it all up and add to the stew, incorporate gently.

Chop up the chilli pepper and add that in too, or a few dried chilli flakes if you prefer. Finally, chop up a generous handful of fresh, fragrant coriander and add to the dish, reserving a few sprigs to adorn the dish.

Light the candles and serve with a good ol' blob of crème fraiche. Mmmm, yummy and heart-warming.

'From every pore exudes a hunger and for that passion I can't wait, for what you offer to me does more than satiate.'

Fiona Collins

Cod Loin with Ibérico Chorizo Sausage and Beetroot Mash

"Prejumptuous cod"

This is a great dish for a quick supper and the beetroot will give you a good shot of vitamin C and loads of energy. The cod, as with all fish and shellfish, promotes sexual well-being, given the wealth of minerals, amino acids and heart-healthy fats to be found in fish. The cayenne pepper is a great circulation booster too. In Michael van Straten's book, *Good Mood Food*, he coins cayenne as a sexy spice. Van Straten also maintains that it gives long-term benefits to men's sexual prowess. Anyone for a quickie?

What to do it with:

2 cod loins
1 small chorizo sausage
1 lemon, sliced
1 pat of butter (50g)
Sea salt & ground black pepper
1 tsp cayenne pepper

Ready-made tray of beetroot mash (Sainsbury's)
200g mashed potato
2 tsp horseradish
1 tsp multigrain mustard
Fresh chopped chives

How to do it:

Put the 2 cod loins in foil. Chop and crumble the chorizo on top and add the pat of butter. Season with salt, pepper and cayenne.

Lay on the lemon slices. Bake in the oven for 20 minutes at 180°C.

Assuming you have your mashed potatoes at the ready, incorporate the tray of beetroot mash, which you will have heated according to packet instructions.

Now, add the next two ingredients, but not the chives just yet.

Arrange into a heart shape or use a mould; sprinkle the chives on top, the green with the red looks stunning. Enjoy, precious partners.

'Cooking is love, made visible.'

Anon.

Bœuf Bourguignon with Thyme, Garlic and Red Wine

"Thyme to get your Bourgy-on"

This succulent and delicious slow-cooked delight will do wonders for you. *Thymus linearis* Benth., is just one species of thyme, in over 400. This wonderful aromatic herb boasts many medicinal and beneficial properties. In a 2013 study, the active substance, carvacrol, was shown to affect neuron activity, which boosted the subjects' feelings of well-being. When many sufferers of ED experience depression and low mood, thyme is a good-news telegram, as it has a positive effect on mood and feelings. I am so excited as I write this; the humble onion has so many health benefits, I cannot possibly list them all. However, one of them is that it helps cardiovascular disease and was even used to treat infertility in women. Great news if you two are trying to get pregnant!

What to do it with:

(This is to serve 6, but you can always freeze the leftovers)
1 kg braising steak of good quality cut into cubes
5 tbsp olive oil
200g bacon lardons or pancetta lardons (I used the latter)
1 large red onion, finely chopped or if you like it rough...
2 garlic cloves, finely chopped
75 cl bottle of shiraz
3 tbsp tomato purée with chilli
1 cube beef stock
3 bay leaves
4 sprigs of fresh-torn thyme
1 oz butter
200g chestnut mushrooms, chopped into quarters.

How to do it:

Brown the meat in the olive oil in batches, about 3 minutes on each side. Remove from pan and go on to fry the lardons for about 3 minutes and spoon over the meat, which you will have placed in the slow cooker.

In the residue oil from the meat and lardons, fry the onion until transparent or, if you prefer, you may caramelise the onion. Add the garlic after a few minutes and fry for a further 3 to 4 minutes.

Flop the onion mix over the meat, slosh in all the wine and squirt the purée from the tube, measuring, as I do, by sight, or if you are more anal, take out a tablespoon and measure it that way!
Add the dissolved stock cube with approximately 300 ml water.

Add then, the torn thyme and bay leaves and stir in gently.

Cover and cook on the low setting for 3 to 4 hours. Half an hour before, heat the butter and if you wish, add another clove of chopped garlic to the mushrooms and stir-fry for 5 minutes over medium to low heat. Tip these into the dish and mix in with a wooden spoon. Serve over rice, pasta or mashed potatoes, with a crunchy side of steamed red cabbage, broccoli or just a green salad, the choice is yours. Remember lovers, this dish is both beneficial, health-wise and totally tasty!

'My weaknesses have always been food and men. In that order.'

Dolly Parton

A Tuna Pasta Bake

"Tuna know what I like"

This little pasta dish is quite a delight, it has the crunch of flaked almonds to delight your senses and within those almonds, lie a buffet of nutrients: calcium for strong bones... yes, *that* bone too! Also, magnesium, folic acid and zinc, all energy-giving minerals. The dried chipotle chilli flakes are a sure-fire way to get the circulation pumping. The perfect bouquet of oregano gives the dish a delicate aroma and has the added benefit of promoting cardiovascular function, keeping the arteries clear of calcium deposits as well as fighting off the dreaded, "man-flu", which, as we are all acutely aware, cannot only kill an erection, but the man himself, or so he says!

What to do it with:

1 can of tuna (responsibly sourced, always)
1 tbsp chipotle chilli flakes or any chilli flakes
2 tsp dried oregano (or as much as you prefer)

2 tsp capers
1 tbsp flaked almonds
Farfalle pasta for 2 (about 400g)
Fresh basil to garnish
For the roux: 2 tbsp butter, 2 tbsp flour and 100g grated cheese of your choice.

How to do it:

Turn on the oven to 180°C if it's a fan oven or 200°C if not. Boil your pasta till al dente, about 10 minutes. Drain and set aside. Make a roux, add 100g grated cheese and 2 tsp multigrain mustard; this only takes 2 or 3 minutes.

In a saucepan, mix into your pasta, reserving a third to add on top with some extra grated cheese. Add the tuna and stir until well coated, sprinkle in your dried ingredients, then the capers and lastly the flaked almonds. At this point you can taste for crunch, if you like it super crunchy, just add more almonds.

Tip the whole lot into a baking dish, if you've a heart-shaped croquet, even better. Then pour over your cheese sauce, fold in till you feel satisfied and sprinkle a little grated cheddar and parmesan on the top and bake for 25 to 30 minutes. Serve with a bit on the side, as in a salad or thinly sliced radishes, as they are so pretty as well as crunchy!

'He was a bold man who first ate an oyster.'

Jonathan Swift

Rigatoni with Garlic, Chilli & Rocket

"Rocket Man"

I give you once again a speedy, yet sumptuous meal. Allow me to bang on about the benefits of garlic, in my magic number of 3 key facts. What was it about the ancient Egyptians, in the days of yore? Time was certainly put to good use, erecting all sorts of things, and they must have been concerned with stamina because these guys used garlic to boost it. Garlic has been said to stop the formation of new fatty deposits, nano plaques, inside arterial walls, including the arteries that lead to the penis. This is good news for achieving an erection.

Garlic is also good in the prevention of the dreaded "man-flu".

What to do it with:

200g dried rigatoni (or any pasta)
2 tbsp olive oil plus extra to serve

47

2 cloves garlic, minced or crushed
1 tsp chilli flakes
2 tbsp chopped parsley (helps to combat garlic breath)
¼ cup freshly grated or shaved parmesan

How to do it:

Cook the pasta in a large pan of salted boiling water for 1 minute less than the packet instructions. Whilst that's cooking, heat the olive oil in a wok or frying pan. Cook the garlic and chilli flakes over low heat for 2 minutes, or until golden, but not browned.

Season with salt and pepper. Reserve ¼ cup of the remaining water then drain the pasta. Add the hot pasta and reserved water to the wok and toss together with the parsley. Then add 3 tablespoons of the parmesan and toss again. Transfer to serving bowls and drizzle with a little more of the oil together with the remainder of parmesan, add a pinch of salt and enjoy on a bed of rocket leaves.

'Food, far more than sex, is the great leveller. Just as every king, prophet, warrior, and saint had a mother, so every Napoleon, every Einstein, even Jesus, had to eat.'

Betty Fussell

Wok-Fried Salmon with Colourful Plum Tomatoes & Parsley

"Salmon to love"

This is quick, easy and delicious. Simple salmon boasts a bevvy of benefits, in particular, it is, according to *Men's Health* magazine, one of the finest natural resources for selenium, the essential mineral for sperm production.

This succulent fish is high in Omega-3 fatty acids, which play a critical part in heart health and good circulation, keeping the male organ primed for performance.

Tomatoes were featured in a *Daily Mail* article, being touted as one of the everyday foods that boost sex drive. They are packed with the nutrient lycopene, which is known for improving cardiovascular function and relaxing the blood vessels; especially beneficial for men when it comes to combatting erectile dysfunction. Pretty parsley has a wealth of antioxidants and nutrients like vitamins, A, K and C; all support heart, kidney and bone health.

What to do it with:

2 tbsp extra virgin olive oil
20g unsalted butter
2 salmon steaks
Seasoning
2 handfuls of plum tomatoes (I used yellow and red for a colour burst)
1 clove of garlic (minced)
Juice of half a lemon
1 handful of parsley to garnish (use dried if you prefer)
1 tbsp fish sauce
400g pak choi, separated and sliced in halves
150g sugar snap peas

How to do it:

Generously season the salmon fillets with salt and pepper. Put the oil and butter in your wok or frying pan, over medium heat, swirling around until melted and foaming. Then, turn up the heat and add the fillets, skin side down. Fry for about 3 minutes until skin is crisp. Flip over and, with the heat turned down, add the sliced tomatoes and minced garlic. Cook for a further 3 minutes, gently stirring your plums, until they're glistening with oil and butter. Add a little squeeze of lemon and flop onto plates.

'I miss you like the sunset, full of pure bliss, I miss you and love's sweet kiss.'

Fiona Collins

A Thai Fish Curry

"Thai me on tonight"

This is super easy, luscious and exotic, the juice from limes and the hint of ginger jolts you awake and leaves your tongue tingling and begging for more. Ginger, according to a study in the *International Journal of Cardiology*, is excellent for improving blood flow and assisting artery health. A mere teaspoon a few times a week is all you need to reap the heart-healthy benefits. Limes and other citrus fruits contain vitamins B and C, which are essential to sex drive and sexual health. They are a great source of folic acid which boosts fertility. Insider Health conducted a recent study and found that couples who had more fish in their diets had sex more frequently than couples who consumed less. The study also found that couples who ate more fish were more likely to become pregnant. This is great news for those of you trying to start a family, and for those of you who aren't, there is always contraceptive options! The lowdown is that fish is a sex-boosting food, as is *all* seafood.

51

What to do it with:

Olive oil
2 spring onions (use scissors to cut into two-centimetre bits)
2 banana shallots, sliced
1 tsp grated ginger
1 clove garlic
4 tbsp Thai red curry paste
400ml fish or vegetable stock
Juice of 2 limes
200ml can coconut milk
1 tbsp fish sauce
400g pak choi separated and sliced in halves
150g sugar snap peas
150g mini sweetcorn sliced lengthways
4 frozen white fish fillets
Brown basmati rice to serve on
Coriander leaves to dress

How to do it:

Turn oven on to 175°C. Whilst it's heating up, place the fillets in some foil, rub with a little olive oil and splash over a little of the coconut milk and add a dob of butter. Set aside, till the oven is ready. Once heated place in the oven for 25 minutes, checking halfway and then turn.

In a wok, heat the olive oil and toss in the first 4 ingredients. Once beginning to sizzle, about 3 minutes, dollop in the paste and stir-fry for about a minute. In with the vegetable stock, lime juice, coconut milk and fish sauce, and give it all a good stir.

Toss in the vegetables, pak choi, peas and sweetcorn and bring to a gentle boil, then simmer for 5 minutes.

Take the fish out of the oven and, using tongs or a spatula, carefully place it into the wok. Break up the fish gently and allow the fish to soak in the juices, before serving on a bed of rice.

'Cooking is like making love, it should be entered into with abandon, or not at all.'

Harriet Van Horne

An Eton Mess

"Hot & Sticky"

You can have this dessert with hot or cooled strawberries; I prefer mine cooled, keeping the heat for the boudoir. The strawberry, like the cherry, is a suggestive berry, red and juicy... perfect for popping delicate spoonfuls onto a wanton tongue. Plentiful in the summer and right up through an often chilly November. Bursting with flavour, these iconic delights are high in vitamin C, which has been touted as being libido boosting. Studies have revealed that strawberries can protect men against prostate cancer. The seeds in the strawberries contain high levels of zinc, which, it is said, can seriously boost your sex drive, whey hey!

What to do it with:

200g fresh strawberries
2 tbsp caster sugar
2 tbsp double cream

2 tbsp elderflower cordial
1 small bunch of mint finely chopped (reserve a few whole leaves to garnish)
4 meringue nests (I use Sainsbury's "Taste the difference") bashed up
Few sprigs of fresh mint

How to do it:

Preheat the oven to 180°C. Chop strawberries into quarters or halves, whichever you prefer. Lay in a baking dish and gently sprinkle over the sugar, bathing each strawberry till nicely covered. Bake for 25 minutes, then take out and leave to cool.
Gently whisk the double cream, but not as so it's stiff, just to soft peaks. Add the cordial and whisk again.
Pour in your cooled strawberries and make a mess with them and the crumbled meringue nests, stir till it gets nice and messy. Sprinkle in the mint and serve in dessert glasses.

"Dieting is food that makes you sad when you eat it"

Anon

An Orange Chocolate Loaf Cake

"Orange you glad I love you"

It's no coincidence that the orange is round, slightly egg-shaped. These juicy fruits have been scientifically researched in relation to fertility and have been found to improve the chance of getting pregnant. Citrus fruits in general have been linked to sperm health, rendering your "swimmers" faster and less likely to clump together. Even if you're not aiming to start a family or increase the existing one, oranges can help with both fatigue and low libido. Cocoa increases blood flow, which helps with stimulation during sex, and also releases your feel-good chemicals, such as serotonin and dopamine. A sweaty run releases the latter-mentioned chemicals, which is why jogging is addictive. The good news is, you don't have to start training for the next marathon when you can take her in your arms and run up to the bedroom. This simple, easy loaf cake will satisfy your sugar craving and make you want to jump for joy.

What to do it with:

Parchment paper
150g soft unsalted butter
50ml golden syrup
180g brown sugar or muscovado
150g plain flour (I use gluten-free, "Freee" by Doves Farm)
½ tsp bicarbonate of soda
30g cocoa powder (I love Green & Black's organic)
2 free-range eggs (always try to buy free-range, tastier)
2 oranges
1- 2 lb loaf tin

How to do it:

First, you want to line your loaf tin with parchment paper, you could grease the tin, but I find no matter how much you grease a pan, it still sticks.
Pop the oven on, 170°C
Now beat the butter or stir with a firm hand and pour in the sugar and then the syrup; get a nice creamy texture going on there.
Once you've measured the flour, bicarb and cocoa together, make a well and add in the butter cream. Beat the eggs separately and tip them into the mix. Now give it all a good blending, either with an electric whisk or manually.
If you have a food processor, attach the grater and simply add the quartered oranges, ensuring pips have been removed, as you do not want an upset tummy. This will give you both the juice and zest necessary.
Using a silicone spatula, if handy, to scoop the mix into the loaf tin. Bake for 40 minutes. Allow to cool and enjoy with a cup of hot chocolate for a double whammy. Wham Bam, thank you both sir and madam.

'Feed the soul and the heart is fed.'

Fiona Collins

Coconut, Apricot & Cinnamon Balls

"Bedtime Balls or Balls to Bedtime"

There is something so sensual about making these versatile volups, it's almost tantric. Fun to mould together with wet hands. Apricots, especially dried ones, have amazing health benefits. As well as helping to reduce blood pressure, they are also beneficial for the treatment of anaemia due to their high iron content. Equally, they are fabulous for anti-ageing as they contain beta-carotene, which your body converts to vitamin A (retinol). Absolutely excellent for plumping up the skin and other things!

What to do it with:

200g dried apricots
50g desiccated coconut
50g pumpkin seeds

25g black sesame seeds
50g porridge oats
50ml water
4 tbsp maple syrup
1 tsp cinnamon

How to do it:

In a food processor, pulse together all your dried ingredients. Ever so slowly, add the water; you may need more if the mixture looks, or feels, too dry to mould! Pulse once again, then add the maple syrup and pulse till blended.
Remove the blade from the unit. Now then, with slightly dampened hands, wet with water, scoop out just enough mixture to fit into the palm of your hand and simply roll into a bite-sized ball.

Once you've run out of mixture for making the balls, place them onto a tray or plate and place them in the fridge for an hour or overnight, to feast on with your morning coffees perhaps?

These little balls of delight are perfect for packing into a picnic or having as a light, energy-enhancing snack.

'If a man can't lick me like an ice-cream cone, then I ain't interested.'

Mae West

Fiona Lou Collins

Chocolate Banana & Hazelnut Loaf Cake

"Nuts about the banana"

There is such simplicity in making a perfectly good cake in a loaf
tin, it's less faff and tastes just as delicious, plus the cubes of
chocolate placed on top when it's hot out of the oven melt slowly
over it, and can then be gently spread, and et voila! chocolate
icing. *Always* use the best available chocolate; skimping is best
saved for G-strings! Let's talk about chocolate. Two chemicals that
simulate being in love linger in chocolate: serotonin and
phenylethylamine. They are also mild stimulants and mood
boosters. A BBC study found that participants who let chocolate
melt on their tongues had higher pulse rates and brain activity
similar to that experienced during passionate kissing. The above
is only true where dark chocolate is concerned, which is why you
will find dark chocolate in this recipe. Chocolate *is* one of the
classic aphrodisiacs, what more is there to say?

60

What to do it with:

2 large ripe bananas, peeled and mashed
175g brown or caster sugar
175g plain flour
1 tsp baking powder
1 tsp bicarbonate of soda
1 tsp vanilla essence
2 large eggs
50ml milk
100ml sunflower oil
90g bar Green & Black's dark chocolate broken into chunks
Loaf tin 2 lbs
Baking parchment

How to do it:

Turn the oven on 160°C. Line the loaf tin with parchment paper or you can use tin foil.

Mash the bananas to a thick yoghurt consistency. Add the sugar and vanilla essence.

Separate the eggs and add just the yolks with the milk to the mashed bananas, whisk this all together gently by hand.

In a separate bowl, measure your dried ingredients. Make a well in the middle and pour in the banana mixture. Using a spatula or wooden spoon, fold these two worlds together, till you have no dry patches of flour showing through.

Whisk the egg whites till they're a little stiff but not peaked, then add slowly to the batter.

Reserve half a dozen cubes of the chocolate, the rest throw into your batter and once again stir to roughly incorporate.

Scrape the contents into the loaf tin, pop in the oven for 1 hour or until a toothpick prick comes out clean.

Carefully place the cubes of chocolate on top of your steaming hot loaf and allow it to melt. Once melted, spread over the loaf cake as you would icing. Allow to cool on a wire rack. Enjoy warm or refrigerate for an hour or so. I like mine still warm with a scoop of vanilla ice cream; how will you eat yours?

'Love me, love my food.'

Fiona Collins

Coconut Truffles

"Love Balls"

Coconut Cures, a book written by Bruce Fine in 2005, declares that coconut water is a natural alternative to Viagra, as it stimulates and strengthens reproductive function in men and increases libido. There are other assertions, although not scientifically proven, that coconut affects libido and virility. According to Healthline.com research, the chain of triglycerides in coconut are metabolised by the body in such a way that it helps release energy and can even promote fat loss when eaten in place of long-chain, saturated fats from animal foods. These oh so edible, delicious and filling delights have only 2 ingredients, yes, love bugs, it only takes 2! Five minutes to prepare and pop in the fridge. I absolutely just love it when a recipe looks as if a highly trained chef took hours to prepare it. You may want to use latex gloves or similar, spray with a little oil too, as this is a sticky business.

What to do it with:

3/4 can condensed milk
1 200g bag desiccated coconut (flakes)
1 pair of loving hands
Makes 8 big balls (roughly)

How to do it:

In a mixing bowl pour in the coconut flakes and slowly incorporate the condensed milk. Reserve a side plate of flakes for rolling.

Use a spatula or a tablespoon, whichever works best. I use a tablespoon as that's roughly the amount of mix required to make each truffle ball.

Pop on gloves if using, or just spray your hands with a spritz of cooking oil, to prevent sticking; resist the urge to lick your – or anyone else's – fingers!

Once mixed, put some of the mixture onto the spoon and pop it into your hand. Roll in your palm to get the ball rolling, or moulded, I mean.

Roll each ball delicately on the plate until there is enough coconut to cover them evenly. Place on a tray, or use a small chopping board covered with tin foil and refrigerate for an hour or so.

'Let food be thy medicine and medicine be thy food.'

Hippocrates

Peanut Butter Chocolate Truffles

"Chocolate Balls"

The combination of chocolate and peanut butter is true genius, just ask the people at Reese's, the inventors of peanut butter chocolate cups. These delicious bites will give you an instant energy burst and an orgasm on the tongue. The dark chocolate has stimulant properties, in that it aids blood flow to the nether parts. It also releases serotonin and dopamine in the brain which boosts good mood; to feel good is to feel sexy. Peanut butter is especially good for men as peanuts are a natural and rich source of L-arginine. This amino acid helps improve sexual function as it relaxes blood vessels. It is the L-arginine itself that may help with erectile dysfunction due to its effect on the southward flowing blood vessels. Oats are an excellent source of vitamin B and are included in the testosterone-boosting-foods group.

What to do it with:

130g oatmeal
65g honey
30g peanut butter (has to be smooth)
Baking tray covered with foil or parchment paper
150g dark chocolate (use highest cocoa content)

How to do it:

Mix together the first 3 ingredients; you may wish to add a tiny bit of water to get the mix malleable.
Using a tablespoon, scoop enough to cover the palm of one hand and then simply, roll into balls and place on a baking tray, with whichever cover you will be using.
Once all used up and the balls are formed, place them in the fridge for 30 minutes.

Bash up the chocolate and in a Pyrex jug or bowl, melt over medium heat for around 3 minutes. When perfectly melted, the chocolate will be glossy, smooth and run easily off the end of a spoon.

Remove the peanut butter balls from the fridge. Then take each one and gently roll it around with a spoon or a fork to completely cover it with the chocolate before placing back onto the tray. Alternatively drizzle the chocolate as I've done in the picture.

Once you have all the balls covered, simply return to the fridge and allow 30 minutes or an hour to enjoy as dessert or an energy-boosting snack.

'It's funny, in a way the actor is a writer. It's not like the two things are so separate as to be like apples and oranges. The writer and the actor are one.'

Sam Shepard

Orange Caraway Seed Loaf

"Get Carawayed"

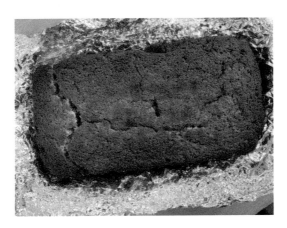

There's nothing like a good loaf, I'm not loafing around here. The cosy and enticing aroma that will permeate throughout your home, with this recipe, is nothing to loaf about. The heady scent is almost like a mating call, or if not feeling so energetic, a call to cuddle up? Many seeds contain a selection of sexual health benefits, even fertility benefits. High levels of zinc promote fertility and boost sex hormone levels. Caraway seeds go a step further than their sidekicks, sesame or cumin, and are claimed to help with weight loss and improve gut health too. Oranges have an innumerable number of health benefits: they are great for a glowing complexion and for bolstering the immune system, meaning you will look and feel more beautiful. Orange peel is where the real gems of this fruit lay, which is great news as my recipe uses *all* the rind and *all* the orange. The peel is packed with vitamin C, B6, folate and calcium.

What to do it with:

1 orange scrubbed to remove any pesticides
175g unsalted butter
100g caster sugar
100g muscovado or any brown sugar
150g plain flour or gluten-free plain flour
2 tsp baking powder
1 tsp cinnamon
50g ground almonds
25g desiccated coconut
5 tsp caraway seeds
2 eggs
2 tbsp golden syrup
1 tsp vanilla essence

How to do it:

Line a loaf tin or just grease or both!
If you have a NutriBullet juicer, as I do, pop the orange into it, but first ensure you have sliced it in half and *removed* the pips, these can be poisonous when using a juice extractor.
Preheat the oven to 180°C. Have your lined loaf tin at the ready.
Cream the butter and sugar together till fluffy and light.
Using a mixing bowl, tip in the flour, baking powder, cinnamon, ground almonds, caraway seeds and coconut. Give that all a good mix with a wooden spoon or spatula.
In a separate bowl, crack in and whisk the eggs. Add the golden syrup and vanilla essence, once whisked.
Incrementally add the wet ingredients to the dry. I do one tablespoon at a time and using an electric whisk, begin to slowly incorporate all the ingredients. This helps to avoid flour flying everywhere, making a mess, which is better left for the bedroom!
Once all is combined, scrape into the loaf tin; I use a silicone spatula to get every last bit. Bake for 45 minutes, but check at the

35-minute mark: it should be browning nicely and smelling heavenly.

'Hard work should be rewarded by good food.'

Ken Follett

A Chocolate, Summer Fruits, Trifle

"When Harry met Sally"

I invented this trifle and without realising it, caused a sensation of multiple orgasms on the tongue, a bit like the restaurant scene, where Meg Ryan's banging on the table and making out that she is having an orgasm. Hence the name of this dish... oh stop it, you're making me blush!

Dark chocolate... it *has* to be dark, the higher cocoa content the better. You can't stand dark chocolate? That's OK, use milk chocolate but *only* if you insist! I'm going to bang on about chocolate as I know there are a *lot* of you lovers out there who go nuts for chocolate! Drum roll please for chocolate, but only really dark chocolate is an aphrodisiac. Yes, yes, yes! According to an article in *The New York Times* by Anahad O'Connor. "... scientists ascribe the aphrodisiac qualities of chocolate to two chemicals, it contains". These chemicals are known as tryptophan—a building block of serotonin, a brain chemical involved in sexual arousal and phenylethylamine, a stimulant released by the brain when people fall in love. A little hint, regarding the summer fruits compote, you can use tinned strawberries, or cherries or any other fruit you fancy.

What to do it with:

200g chocolate cake
Summer fruits compote
1 tin custard
30g Shavings of dark or milk chocolate
Whipping cream

How to do it:

Use a glass dessert dish or a wine glass to layer the chocolate loaf on the bottom.
Drizzle over the summer fruits compote. Add shavings of chocolate.
Spoon in the custard and again, add shavings of chocolate.
Keep layering until your dish or glass is full and top with the whipping cream.
Sprinkle the last of the chocolate shavings on top. And make sure the windows are shut!

'Trifles make perfection, and perfection is no trifle'

Michelangelo

Berry Oat Muffins

"Berry nice to see you"

These little muffins are like fireworks, bursting with flavour, and exploding with goodness. What's more, they taste delicious. I have embellished a recipe I found in *200 Light Cakes and Desserts (Hamlyn-Askews & Holts-2015)*. Oats are so good for you, boosting your sex drive if scientists are to be believed. The San Francisco Institute for Advanced Study of Human Sexuality found that men who include oats in their diet had stronger sex drives. This may be down to their vitamin B rich content. Furthermore, B6 suppresses the production of oestrogen, which helps testosterone levels to *rise*... no need for further explanation.

I salute you, oh "one-eyed Anaconda of love!" **Fact bite:** The anaconda, indigenous to South America, is one of the heaviest and longest extant snake species. I digress, thinking of the trouser snake!

Berries, all of them, are excellent as a source of vitamin C and have antioxidant properties. Energy-boosting berries are one of the best things to eat for all sorts of reasons, one major one is protection against prostate cancer. Thank you, humble strawberry. (Don't worry if it's not the right season, even if it's wintertime, you can use frozen berries.)

What to do it with:

250g plain flour
150g caster sugar
1 tbsp baking powder
50g oats
100g ground almonds
2 tsp ground cinnamon
1 beaten egg
200ml milk
50ml coconut oil or vegetable oil
1 tsp vanilla essence
200g frozen mixed berries

How to do it:

Line a one dozen cavity muffin tray with non-stick paper cases. Pop the oven on at 180°C.

Simply blend together all the dried ingredients, using a wooden spoon or similar to incorporate.

Beat egg and add together with the oil and vanilla essence and slowly mix or beat into the dry mixture, to make a smooth dough.

Fold in the mixed berries and using an ice-cream scoop or spoon, dollop the mixture into paper muffin cases. Be careful not to overfill as this will cause oozing, and we want things rising.

Pop into the oven once ready, and bake for 25 minutes. I do the toothpick test here again. Prick it into the hot muffin, and if it comes out clean, it's done, ready to be eaten hot or chilled. Gorgeous.

'I only drink Champagne on two occasions, when I am in love and when I am not.'

Coco Chanel

A Persian Love Cake

"Persian Passion Cake"

Gods and Goddesses, I give you Persian Passion Cake. This is adapted from **BBC** Food online mag. I had to break from my normal quick and easy approach to recipes; if this cake were a woman, she'd be high maintenance, but worth it.

This is a cake truly worthy of offering up to the gods, one bite of this and you will be soaring the heavens. Sexologist **Dr R Gupta** claims that cardamom is a spice that contains high levels of cineole which increases blood flow to both male and female sexual areas, increasing your desire. Cardamom has balancing and detoxifying properties.

In Ayurvedic medicine, it can be used to increase energy levels. Cardamom is prescribed by Chinese doctors to revitalise sexual desire; it has a stimulant effect on overall well-being.

The aroma produced from the pods is quite intoxicating in itself. Orange, lemon and almonds guarantee a cake that's moist and delicious, just what your mouth has been waiting for. You want more, you know you do.

What to do it with:

200g unsalted butter, sliced and softened
220g golden caster sugar
4 eggs
1 lemon, juice & grated zest
1 small orange, juice & grated zest
2 tsp rosewater or you can use rose tea
150g plain flour
2 tsp baking powder
½ tsp bicarbonate of soda
12 ground cardamom pods
100g ground almonds
100g ground pistachios (this takes a while)
3 tbsp sour cream or plain yoghurt

To adorn:

150g icing sugar
Juice of ½ lemon
1 tbsp orange juice
Dash of rosewater
1 tbsp dried rose petals
25g nibbed pistachios

How to do it:

Preheat oven to 170°C. Brush your cake tin or Bundt tin with melted butter, dust with flour and shake to coat the tin, turn upside down and slap out any excess flour.

Unless you are lucky enough to find ground pistachios you will have to shell them and grind them in a NutriBullet, if you have one, otherwise, a pestle and mortar will do the job.

Using an electric hand whisk, blend together the butter and sugar, whisking for at least 5 minutes. Add the eggs one at a time, whisk, whisk, whisk. You may need a spatula to scrape down the bowl, this can get messy! Add the lemon and orange zest and juice with the rosewater and mix again.

Sift the flour, baking powder, bicarbonate of soda and cardamom into the bowl. Add the ground almonds, pistachios and sour cream/yoghurt and mix in well. Spoon all of it into your tin. Bang it down gently to even the mixture.

Bake for 35 minutes, ensuring it's well risen and that a toothpick comes out clean—you remember the prick test, right? Place on a wire rack and allow to cool completely.

To adorn:

Beat the icing sugar with enough lemon and orange juice to make a smooth, thick but pourable icing. Add a few drops of rosewater to taste.

 Carefully spoon the icing over the cake, let it drizzle on down. Leave for about 3 minutes and the icing will begin to set. Whilst it's still sticky, scatter with rose petals and pistachios, leave to set again, if you can.

Serve it as it is for the taste sensation, once you've marvelled over how aesthetically pleasing this cake truly is.

'Life's short, eat dessert first.'

Anon.

A Pineapple Pavlova

"Pine no more, I'm yours"

This is simply delicious, low-calorie and luscious. This will need to go in the freezer for at least 4 hours, so plenty of time for teasing, foreplay and trying for that baby? If your libido is lagging, jump on the Pineapple Express! Pineapples contain high levels of vitamin C and thiamine, which are great for an energy boost. Hormones get happier with thiamine, and the manganese within them helps your man get frisky. If you *are* trying for a baby, pineapples are nutrient-rich in copper and several B vitamins, which are important during pregnancy. An added benefit of eating pineapple is its effect on the taste of your "lady garden" or whatever you choose to call it! I have added a few mixed frozen berries to this dessert for colour and texture.

What to do it with:

1 can (400g) sliced pineapple in syrup
Pinch of ground cinnamon
1 tsp vanilla essence
1 tbsp caster sugar
150g half-fat crème fraiche
50g frozen mixed berries (optional)
4 meringue nests, crushed

How to do it:

Drain the pineapple and use 100 ml of the juice or syrup to place into a small saucepan. Stir the cinnamon, vanilla and sugar into the syrup and heat for 5 minutes, until the sugar has dissolved. Add the pineapple and berries to the syrup and mix through the crème fraiche, gently folding in the crumbled meringue.

Place all into a Tupperware or similar container and place in the freezer for 4 hours, minimum. This will ensure the dessert is softly frozen. Decorate with a spare berry and enjoy, my lovelies.

'A party without cake is just a meeting.'

Pat Conroy

Cardamom, Oat and Orange Cookies

"So, you like oats?"

Oats so good for you and in a cookie? These oats so delicious cookies can be grabbed for a breakfast substitute on a lazy weekend when you may want to sow your morning "oats"? They are high in zinc which can increase testosterone levels, which, in turn, heightens sexual desire in both genders.

Oats are a complex carbohydrate, giving you matching stamina for your passion.

Avena sativa (wild oats) are considered an aphrodisiac, due to the L-arginine found within them. Like a natural Viagra, L-arginine helps penile blood vessels relax, essential to maintaining an erection and reaching orgasm. With all this good news, I recommend eating these biscuits in bed!

Juicy and gorgeous—yes you too, but I was talking about the oranges. Being fully loaded with vitamin C, they help reduce your stress level, a contributing low-libido factor. Oranges contain the phytonutrient hesperidin, which increases blood flow too. Cardamom, that fragrant spice, increases your energy and relieves fatigue. Let's do this, love bugs.

What to do it with:

12 cardamom pods
100g plain flour
½ tsp bicarbonate of soda
50g ground oats
1 tsp ground cinnamon
100g slightly salted butter
50g golden caster sugar
50g dark brown sugar
1 egg
½ tsp vanilla extract
2 tbsp maple or golden syrup
1 medium orange, juice and zest

How to do it:

Line a large baking sheet with parchment paper, or foil can be used too, shiny side down.

Smash the cardamom pods in a pestle and mortar; discard the shells and finely grind the seeds. Lovingly sift the flour, adding the soda and oats and spice to a large mixing bowl.

In another bowl - large preferably - beat the butter and sugars until fluffy and light. Scrape the sides of the bowl with a spatula, silicone works best.

Add the egg, vanilla and syrup and beat until smooth. Incorporate this with the dry mixture in the larger of the bowls, mix manually together before using your electric whisk, and whisk for about a minute.

Add the orange and zest and whisk for just 30 seconds to incorporate, then scoop tablespoons or ping-pong-sized balls of the mixture onto the baking sheet. Cover and chill for 1 hour, or 20 minutes in the freezer.

Preheat oven to 175°C. Remove the cookies from fridge or freezer, uncover and pop in the oven for 20-25 minutes, or until they are going golden around the edges. Allow 10 minutes to cool down.

"I thought about losing weight once, but I don't like losing"

Anon

A Pomegranate, Apricot and Ginger Slice

"Don't be ginger"

This wonderful combination is a sensation on the palate, the bitterness of the pomegranate ignites the sweet taste. Like glistening jewels of a coveted crown, pomegranate seeds and their juice increase sexual desire and improve memory and mood. In ancient times, many civilisations used the juice as a natural aphrodisiac. The seeds are high in polyphenols, which can protect your immune system and boost mood. They have several micronutrients, such as flavones; key players in creating sex hormones and improving erectile function. Apricots have many health benefits, which impacts overall health because naturally if you feel good, you feel frisky. Eating apricots can improve your skin, your gut health, protect your liver and they are high in potassium, so good news for heart health. Finally, ginger can boost a low sperm count and helps increase blood flow to the testes. This cake, basically, is like medicine that tastes good: eat with no guilty pleasure.

What to do it with:

1 x 8 x 10" baking tray, 2" deep, greased or lined
200g plain flour
1 tsp bicarbonate of soda
100ml milk
1 egg
3 tbsp apricot jam
100ml golden syrup or black treacle
75g unsalted butter
1 inch fresh ginger, grated
200ml pomegranate juice
2 tbsp runny honey
100g packet of pomegranate seeds

How to do it:

Preheat the oven to 170°C. Sift the flour and bicarbonate of soda into a bowl. In a jug, beat the milk and egg together. Put the sugar, syrup and butter in a saucepan to heat until the butter melts and sugar is dissolved. Remove from the heat and add the apricot jam giving it a good stir in.

Slowly blend together with the dry ingredients, using either an electric whisk or a good old-fashioned spoon or spatula.

Just as the mixture is all nicely blended, sprinkle in the freshly grated ginger or use a couple of slices of chopped stem ginger. Pop in the oven and bake for half an hour. Test with a skewer; if it's still a bit raw, pop back in for a further 5 minutes. Leave to cool.

To make the topping, pour the pomegranate juice into a saucepan and bring to the boil, then boil for about 10 minutes until thick and syrupy. Stir in the honey and tumble in the pom seeds, stir once again.

To finish off, remove the cooled cake from its tin and turf onto a breadboard or similar. Drizzle the cake with the topping, slice into small squares to serve.

'Shall I compare thee to a summer's day?'

William Shakespeare

A Flourless Chocolate Pear Torte

"Nothing com-pears to you"

As far as presentation goes, this torte is no feast on the eyes, however, the texture and taste by far make up for its lack of aesthetic pleasure. This will fill your home with the sweet and sultry aroma of a seductive combination of cocoa and chocolate. Chocolate, especially dark and high in cocoa solids (above 70 per cent) is best for all stimulation, mood-boosting and it also has a sexual stimulant effect. Eating chocolate can produce feelings of euphoria and sensual pleasure, as it melts on your tongue. Chocolate contains the chemicals phenylethylamine and serotonin, known to have a positive effect on mood. A study on the consumption of pears and erectile dysfunction has proved that eating the fruit just three times a week can reduce ED by up to 19 per cent. Hopefully, this combination of pear and chocolate will leave you amorous and rampant all night long!

What to do it with:

3 pears, skinned and cored
250ml water
125g caster sugar
100g dark chocolate, chopped
25g unsalted butter
2 egg yolks
1 tsp vanilla extract
4 egg whites
Cocoa powder and icing sugar for dusting

How to do it:

Grease or line a 10-inch cake or quiche tin. Make a syrup by bringing 250 ml water and 125 g sugar to the boil. Poach the pears in the resultant syrup for half an hour. Drain the pears and reserve the syrup. Halve the pears and lay core side down in the cake tin. Put the chocolate and butter in a heatproof jug or bowl and melt together over a pan of simmering water, stirring occasionally.

Beat the egg yolks and sugar together until the mixture is quite stiff. Stir in the melted chocolate and vanilla extract.

Beat the egg whites until they are slightly peaking and fold into the chocolate mixture, gently. Unfurl the entire mix into the cake tin and bake in a preheated oven at 175°C for 40 minutes, or until an inserted toothpick comes out clean. Leave to cool for about 20 minutes then dust with cocoa powder and icing sugar, this will give the cake a festive glow.

Serve with a dollop of whipped cream or vanilla ice cream, use one bowl to share and then dive in again, with a bowl each if you so wish.

"Forget all you've been Torte"

Fiona Collins

Chocolate Cherry Muffins

"Deep in the Forest"

These melt-in-your-mouth dessert muffins are a mimic of my favourite Black Forest gateaux, and are made with succulent cherry compote—I use Bonne Maman. As with all my recipes, to jazz it up with your love life, there is a twist in the ingredients. On this occasion, it's a handful of black sesame seeds. These little sweethearts contain many key health ingredients, such as iron, fibre and calcium. They are instrumental in lowering blood pressure and blood cholesterol levels. According to an article in *Nutrition Review,* people who get more fibre in their diet are at a lower risk of coronary heart disease. This is all good news, as a healthy heart equals healthy circulation. Also featured as a key ingredient are crushed chillies; it's already well known that these hot tamales not only boost blood flow, but are fantastic too, at warding off colds and, dare I mention, "man flu"?

What to do it with:

250g plain flour
100g caster sugar
1 tsp salt
1 tbsp baking powder
2 tsp dried chillies
2 tbsp black sesame seeds
1 jar cherry compote
2 beaten eggs
125g butter (melted)
275g dark or milk chocolate (70% cocoa)
1 tsp cocoa powder
1 tsp vanilla extract

How to do it:

Preheat oven to 180°C. Mix all your dried ingredients together whilst you melt the chocolate in a glass heat-proof bowl over a saucepan. Beat the eggs and add the butter. Create a well in the centre of the flour bowl and pour in all the wet ingredients and beat with an electric or hand whisk. Lastly, add the melted chocolate and stir to mix in gently. Using a muffin tray, line each cavity with muffin cases, I like to use foil ones for this as they are more aesthetically pleasing, but feel free to get creative here; you may even want to fashion your own with brown grease-proof paper... fun to do this together bending over the kitchen table? Once ready, scoop mixture into each muffin case and pop in the oven for 25 minutes or until nicely risen. Serve hot with some vanilla ice cream or enjoy for a naughty sweet breakfast?

'Yummy, yummy, yummy I've got love in my tummy.'

Song lyric

A Banana Loaf

"Bonking good Buckwheat Banana loaf"

So delicious and healthy, my version of banana loaf will fill your tummy with love! Instead of plain flour, I use buckwheat flour which is not a flour at all but a ground seed, so excellent if you have a wheat allergy. Kuttu Atta, which is the fruit from which this "flour" is made, is rich in fibre and Vitamin B. It helps to manage diabetes and lowers blood pressure too. It is warming for your insides and boosts your immune system. Great to eat in winter when we like to snuggle up! The soy milk contains several compounds that are especially important for our men. It's low in calories and total fat and high in protein. Its ratio of high unsaturated to saturated fat promotes healthy heart function. Finally, bananas are a good mood enhancer, containing the amino acid, tryptophan, which helps the production of serotonin in the brain. High in B6, bananas help the body produce fresh haemoglobin—good news for healthy blood flow. Their shape, really, says it all!

What to do it with:

245g buckwheat flour
75g coconut sugar or brown or granulated sugar
1/3 cup maple syrup
2 tsp cinnamon powder
2 tsp baking powder
Pinch of sea salt
4 overripe bananas, mashed
75 ml olive oil or coconut oil
1/3 cup sweetened or unsweetened soy milk
2 tsp vanilla extract

How to do it:

Preheat oven to 180°C.
Firstly, grease up a bread tin, or as I prefer, put foil in, so to just flop out, when cooled!
In a mixing bowl, combine all the dry ingredients and give it a nice gentle stir, that's right; now add your mashed bananas in the middle where you've made a little well for the wet stuff. Mix it all in, till it forms a nice, firm batter.
 Now to encourage in, with a stiff, silicone spatula and bake for 40 minutes. Check at the 30-minute point, to ensure it's not overcooking; it should be just nicely browned on top. If you want to, you can sprinkle some icing sugar, sieved, on top.
Cool for half an hour and enjoy with a cup of your favourite hot drink, like cocoa.

'If you were a banana, I'd peel you'

Fiona Collins

BV - #0043 - 170921 - C38 - 210/148/8 - PB - 9781913839352 - Gloss Lamination

creatures
of habit

Based on the television series created by
Joss Whedon

✦

An illustrated novel by
Tom Fassbender, **Jim Pascoe**,
Brian Horton, and **Paul Lee**

✦

Edited by
Scott Allie

✦

Published by
Mike Richardson

Dark Horse Books™

Designers
JIM PASCOE, LIA RIBACCHI *and* KEITH WOOD

Art Director
MARK COX

NEIL HANKERSON • *Executive Vice President*
ANDY KARABATSOS • *Vice President of Finance*
RANDY STRADLEY • *Vice Presidentt of Publishing*
CHRIS WARNER • *Senior Books Editor*
MICHAEL MARTENS • *Vice President of Marketing*
ANITA NELSON • *Vice President of Sales & Licensing*
DAVID SCROGGY • *Vice President of Product Development*
DALE LaFOUNTAIN • *Vice President of Information Technology*
DARLENE VOGEL • *Director of Purchasing*
KEN LIZZI • *General Counsel*
TOM WEDDLE • *Controller*

March 2002
First edition
ISBN: 1-56971-563-7

1 3 5 7 9 10 8 6 4 2
PRINTED IN CHINA

DEDICATION

To my friends in the Circle of Knowledge and the
Saturday morning basketball crew.
— TOM FASSBENDER

To the late-night coffee-shop regulars who kept me
company in the middle of the night.
— JIM PASCOE

To my wife, Susan.
— BRIAN HORTON

To Brian's wife, Susan.
— PAUL LEE

Special thanks to
GEORGE SNYDER, CAROLINE KALLAS, ALLEN SPIEGEL,
and to DEBBIE OLSHAN *at* TWENTIETH-CENTURY FOX.

This story takes place during **BUFFY THE VAMPIRE SLAYER**'*s sixth season.*

CRAVINGS

"WE ARE SO BAD."

Dawn swayed her hips to the loud beat of the music. She could feel her face getting hot, the sweat dripping along her neck. The heat of the room didn't stop her from dancing, and the anxiety of being there made her smile. Her friend, Melinda, showed equal teenage abandon. Both of them loved letting go. They were all about the rush you get when you're somewhere you know you shouldn't be.

"Oh yeah. *So* bad. What would your sister say if she knew you were here?"

"Melinda. Don't sog my cereal. Buffy's *not* here. And she's *not* going to know."

"Whatever, Summers—guess who *is* here? Crush-a-licious, *right* behind me."

"Tyler Williams? He's, like, a senior. And totally not cute."

"Wrong. *Totally* cute. Don't tell me you don't see any hotties here, girl. Just look around."

Dawn looked around. She still couldn't believe it: they were at Faint, the most talked about party scene in Sunnydale. Melinda had been blabbing about it for weeks, about how it was so underground the organizers changed locations every night and kept the whole thing secret to everyone but those already in the know. When Melinda overheard a group of juniors talking in the girls' room about tonight's whereabouts, she and Dawn knew they *had* to sneak out and sneak in.

Flashing colored lights played over the bodies of dozens of teenagers. Several of the kids held bottles of glowing water, an effect caused by submerged light sticks. They made the water look radioactive. The images and the pounding bass vibrations were starting to mesmerize Dawn. Then her eyes caught the boy with unkempt hair, the guy she'd noticed when they first walked into the warehouse.

"Melinda, check him out over there. Nice. I like the way he's nodding his head. And everybody seems to know him."

"Earth to Dawn—wouldn't you like someone a little more familiar with … soap? I mean, his hair—"

"I dunno … I think it's sexy." The thought made Dawn blush, but she danced it off. Tonight was about letting go, about being a teenager and stuff.

Melinda laughed. "His name's Skeeter. I hear he's baaaad."

"Bad like us?" Dawn gave her friend a little shove. They both giggled.

"Probably not even." Melinda dug around in her purse. She pulled out two cigarettes.

"When did you start smoking?"

"Duh! Since forever." Melinda put one in her mouth and offered the other to Dawn. "I take 'em from my mom. She never knows they're missing."

Dawn took the cigarette and held it awkwardly in her hands. "Buffy would kill me if I did this."

"All the more reason to do it, girl. Besides, you gotta play it cool for Skeeter."

"I hear someone call my name?" Skeeter appeared behind them, his arms draped over their shoulders.

Melinda twisted out from under his sweaty arm. "Hey, Skeeter. I'm Melinda, and this is the fabulous Dawn Summers." She took out a lighter and lit up.

Skeeter turned to face Dawn. "Fabulous, huh?"

"Uh … yeah." Dawn leaned over to light her smoke off her friend's flame.

"Cool, D." Skeeter smiled as he rubbed his bottom lip with his middle finger.

Another girl had appeared next to Skeeter. His eyes immediately went to this girl's large chest, bouncing free without a shirt, cupped in a black lace bra. The way she worked him made it seem like she was leading him to the bathroom or the back of a car.

The cigarette made Dawn choke; the smoke made her eyes water. She wasn't so sure she liked this smoking business, but she liked looking cool. Skeeter was cool, and he played the new girl cool. He reached into his backpack and pulled out a bottled water with a light stick in it. Bra girl grabbed it and instantly shut off the sex appeal. She bopped away without saying a word.

"Sorry, ladies." Skeeter returned his attention to Dawn. She felt the room getting more crowded with people pushing against her on all sides. "Some cats need their candy. So how about you? Are you little pussies happy? You need anything?"

Dawn dropped her cigarette.

Some guy with dreadlocks started to pull Skeeter away.

"See you next time, maybe?" he said, just before dropping them the secret of how to find out where the next Faint would be going down.

"Uh, yeah … sure …" Dawn's heart raced faster than the drum and bass in the air. "We'll be there. Definitely."

"Fabulous."

"Slayer, if this is your idea of a good time, I've got to send you back to fun school."

Spike flicked his cigarette butt into the darkness. He looked up at the autumn moon. A coyote howled.

"You don't have to patrol with me," Buffy said.

"You didn't have to ask me to come along."

Buffy stood still for a moment and took in the silence of the cemetery. These days she felt that whenever she stopped, she could always hear the silence. Normal sounds just faded, drifting away from her, leaving her alone. A certain feeling of forever—one she couldn't shake—lingered in these moments.

She wondered if this was her destiny: to fight vampires forever, while family, friends, and life itself disappeared, the way a vampire's body explodes into dust when you drive a stake through its heart.

She thought about her dad, who walked out on the family years ago. She thought about her mother, who died way too young from complications surrounding a brain tumor. At least she still had Giles. She was glad he was here to watch over things and make sure everyone stayed on track … although, even he seemed to be pushing her away these days, trying to get her to stand on her own. But who wants to be alone?

"Creatures of the night seem to have the night off." Spike lit another cigarette. "Fact is, haven't seen much vamp activity all week."

Buffy patted him on the shoulder. "Well, except for you."

Spike huffed and rolled his shoulders. "Oh, so now I'm *activity*?"

"You are when I'm bored."

Buffy's mind drifted again. Her friends may have thought they pulled her out of a hell dimension when they brought her back from the dead, but *this* place felt like hell. Pain and loneliness. Willow was in love with Tara, and Xander had just announced his engagement to Anya. Who did Buffy have?

"Feeling a tad restless, are we?" Spike leaned up against a marble monument. "Sounds a little like someone else I know."

Buffy gave him the stare. Sure she was restless—she had been through too much, too many times. There had to be something that would help her connect with things again. Something that could break the silence the way a wrinkle of lightning can divide the blackest night sky.

"Was talking about your sister." He eyed her back, waiting again for a reaction. "She's a wild one all right."

"Dawn's fifteen. She's just acting her age. And I'm keeping my eyes on her, thank you very—"

She looked to the side. Another sound had caught her ear, but not a coyote this time. A rustle of leaves, a shuffle of feet. She pulled a stake from the inside of her small denim jacket and began stepping toward the sound.

Spike crossed his arms and smacked his lips. "No sense continuing this conversation with you. Not in this mood, anyway."

Buffy whipped up her hand, silencing him. Scanning the shadows cast by the tombstones, she could feel something coming closer.

"Fine. Just shut me off, like you do with your little sis—"

A hulking mass tackled Spike, sending him to the ground. The attacker sprang to his feet, lifting Spike up by his lapels. The creature screamed: "Blood! Blood! We must have blood!"

Buffy tapped the rampaging vampire on his shoulder. He turned around just in time to get a fist to the face.

"Hey, I have needs too, but I don't go beating up on Spike. Although, that's not a bad idea." She threw a couple more jabs to his face, and, as he stumbled back a couple steps, Spike grabbed him around the neck in a sleeper hold.

"Something wrong with your sniffer, mate? You shoulda known you'll get no blood from me." The rogue's eyes rolled back in his head. His breath came out in coughs.

"Blood! Gotta get a dose of blood!"

Buffy cocked her arm back, ready to finish him off. Something about his mad expression—the vacant eyes, the tremble in his fingertips, the labored breathing—made her pause. Enough time for a second vampire to reach out from the shadows and grab her wrist.

"Victor, quit playing with that blonde puff pastry and get outta here while I've got the girl."

The bones in the new vamp's wrist cracked as Buffy yanked her arm forward, flipping him over her shoulder.

"Yeah, you've got me. Like the Pope's got a wife." She drove the stake through his heart. His body exploded into dust.

The sweaty, crazy vamp elbowed Spike in the gut, broke free of the hold, and took off into the woods. Buffy sprinted after him. It didn't take long for her to catch up. She hit him with a couple combinations, and he ran away again. This time when she caught up to him, she tripped him and got him on his knees.

"Most vamps aren't smart enough to run away from me. You—you don't seem too smart. What gives?"

Pathetic babbling replaced his former madness: "Gotta … get back to the … the boss—"

Spike leaped out of the darkness and took the vamp down with a flying tackle. With a sharp twist of the jaw and a crack of the neck, Spike ripped off his head, turning him to dust.

Buffy stormed over to him. "Spike!"

"You damn well think I'd get some respect from my own kind, but no—elbow to the gut is what I get. Goes to show how eventually everyone turns on you."

Buffy popped him one in the nose. Hard.

"Ow! What the hell?"

"He was babbling about 'the boss.' And I was trying to find out if he meant the typical big, evil, bring-about-apocalypse-here-in-Sunnydale boss. Now, instead of a name, you know what I got?"

Spike rubbed his nose. "Dust?"

"Dust."

"I'm tellin' ya, boss, I sees it with my own eyes. This girl kicked Victor's ass *hard*. It *had* to be the Slayer. Then Danny's gotta lose his head and try to *stop* her, and he's all 'get outta here,' and then she makes some kinda joke about the freakin' Pope, man. I took off, and I don't think they saw me. It was not good. Not good at all, I'm tellin' ya."

The tall, dark vampire just listened to this crazed rambling. He was too angry to speak.

"What are we gonna do about this, boss? Boss …?"

The boss came at him hard. The squirrelly little vamp didn't have time to react. Then it was just the big man alone with his anger.

"Damn players can't get *nothin'* right." He slammed a fist against the wall. He walked into another room of the abandoned single-story house. Torn crimson curtains hung over broken windows set in a lime green wall—someone's idea of style many, many years ago.

A girl with short, choppy, platinum hair lounged in a sunken sofa. A crate of vinyl records sat next to the couch. The girl's white arm dangled over the edge of the sofa, her slender fingers lazily flipping through the LPs. She looked up at the angry boss.

"You dust another one? How many does that make? How many are you going to get rid of before you listen to me?"

"Me and you is old news. I don't know why you still hangin' 'round."

"Maybe because I'm the one with the brains. Now are you ready for a real plan, or are you still going to try to take over Sunnydale's vampire population one drugged-up vamp at a time?"

He stormed back and forth across the room looking for something to smash. "Damn, Velatti, I thought the Slayer 'round here was dead. This better not monkey my plan for a little Sunnydale flavor. Now where the hell'd I put that body? Gotta be enough blood in her for one more hit."

"It's right in front of you, in the corner." Velatti pointed to a crumpled-up, naked, teenage girl. Her body had so many bite marks on it, she looked like she had measles. "You'd be able to think a lot more clearly if you weren't always so high."

He sunk his teeth into the corpse's thigh and began to suck at the weak trickle of blood that flowed from the fresh wound. "Ugh, baby, this blood's gone cold."

Velatti stood up and began to slow dance in the center of the room, grooving to the music in her head. "Imagine a whole building filled with tasty humans all high on your Jube. Imagine how many vamps would turn out for a party like that."

"You can set that up?"

"Parnassus, honey, it's already set up. We just need a human to help us out—and I'm all over it. You get the word out to the vampire population."

Velatti stopped dancing and pointed at him with both her hands. "Think you can swing that?"

He looked up at her, eyes glazed over, blood slopping over his lips and chin.

Buffy walked past the open door to Dawn's room. Considering the hour, she would have expected to see Dawn's light off, not glowing boldly. Worse yet, Dawn stepped away from her closet, her nightshirt just pulled over her head.

"Did the concept of a school night go bye-bye, young lady?"

"Buffy! I … I'm in bed, look." She leaped so hard onto her mattress that the springs sounded like they were going to give way. "Me. Bed. In."

"Okay, cut the cute. Start confessing."

"It … it was a monster. A monster-sized craving for ice cream. By the way, we're out of double-chocolate chocolate chunk."

Dawn gave her big sister a big, smug smile. Buffy turned to go, ready to smack the lights out and leave this argument for some other time. But she stopped and sniffed the air. Her eyes went narrow. She stormed over to the side of the bed and grabbed a handful of Dawn's hair, bringing it up to her nose.

"Were you … smoking?"

"No! I was … My friend, Melinda, was over and she … she was smoking." Dawn pulled her hair back from Buffy and scooted to the other end of the bed. "But we went outside when she … I mean, she didn't smoke in the house."

"Where was Giles?"

"He … he said he was going out, something about a 'stroll' to clear his mind. He's probably on the couch now. Willow and Tara were—"

"Is this what it's been like since I was gone? No rules?"

"Buffy, I'm fifteen! I know right from wrong. My friend's not a crack-head, she just had a cigarette, okay? Besides, Spike smokes."

Buffy's mouth fell open.

"Did I just hear you use Spike as *justification* for *smoking*? Are you *completely* out of your mind?"

"I need to get to sleep. Just get out of my room, okay?"

The silence came up around Buffy again. Again, everything drifted back and seemed so small.

"Fine. Go to bed."

Buffy hit the light switch.

SMALL GIFTS

"OH! HOW ABOUT THIS? Yes, we definitely need one of these."

Anya, beaming with pride, held up a metal pan with a strange buckle on the side. Xander squinted at it, thinking the thing looked more like something from a construction site than anything he had expected to find on the shelves at Crate & Barrel.

"Okay, whatever you say. What is it, anyway?"

"Xander. It's a spring-form pan."

"Right. So, what's it do?" Xander looked down and flipped through the sheaf of papers on the clipboard in his hands, trying not to look too confused. "I mean, where do I write it down on this list?"

"It's for baking, so it'll be under—"

"Hold on, let me guess—*bake*ware. See, I'm getting the hang of this wedding registry thing … I think." Xander scrawled some notes on the list. "What I want to know is how does a vengeance demon-turned-human know what a spring-form pan is?"

"*Martha Stewart*. They're used to make cute little cakes and tortes." Anya put the pan back on the shelf and turned her eyes toward the Calphalon cookware display.

"Since when do you read *Martha Stewart?*"

"Since I've decided that if I'm going to be your wife, I'd better start doing all sorts of wifey things, like cooking and sewing and making arts and crafts we can use to decorate our home."

"Whoa, whoa, whoa. Anya, can we drop down a few gears?"

Anya's hands shot to her hips. Her face started to burn a bright crimson. She leaned in toward Xander and pointed an accusing finger his way. "It seems to me that lately you want to 'drop down a few gears' with *anything* that has to do with *me.*"

"Hold on." Xander set the clipboard on top of an espresso maker. "That's not what I meant!"

Anya stopped walking and turned to face him, arms folded across her chest. "So just what *did* you mean? First you ask me to marry you, but you keep it a big secret. And now that it's not a big secret anymore, you keep saying things that make me feel like you want to avoid nuptial bliss with me. I read about this! This is fear of commitment!"

"Ahn, cut me a little slack. This whole thing is freaking me out. I mean, registering for wedding gifts—stuff that my parents didn't even have—it feels weird. Besides, who's gonna buy us all this stuff? We're the only two people we know who have jobs. This whole domestic-girl curve ball you're throwing at me … it's going to take a little getting used to, that's all."

"Does that mean you still love me and want to enter into blissful nuptials?" She let her arms fall to her sides. Her pout turned from cute to cuter.

"Yes, I want to be blissed. More than anything."

"You're sure?" Her eyes flickered.

"Absolutely sure."

Anya stepped forward and threw her arms around Xander, holding him tight. He returned her hug, sighing with relief.

As they drifted out of the hug, Xander put his hands on both of her shoulders, gave them a little squeeze, took a breath, and said, "I know we both took off work to do this, but—at the risk of bodily harm—can I suggest we quit for the day?"

Anya looked deep into Xander's eyes, searching for any sign of deception. "You promise you'll want to finish up later?"

"Yes, I promise." Xander put one hand over his heart and held up the other hand in his best Boy Scout salute.

Anya sighed. "Okay. I'm feeling weird being away from the Magic Box, anyway. I don't want Giles to think I'm not dedicated to the store … he might *stay*! It's not like I don't like having him around, it's just not fair that a silent partner should be so non-silent."

"No, I don't think we have that in stock, but we do have the *Karatouch Tome*." Giles looked up from the telephone receiver and motioned to Willow to grab a book off a nearby shelf.

"Good save, Giles. I have to say, the *Karatouch* is first rate … as far as tomes go." Willow scanned the shelves for the book.

Buffy was leaning against the bookshelf, staring down at the floor in front of her. Willow wished she knew what to do to cheer Buffy up. Ever since the night Buffy clawed her way out of her own grave, she'd been a little different. Tara, who sat at the table in front of the bookshelf reading from her art history textbook, had told Willow to give it time. Buffy would come around. Willow knew Tara was probably right, but she still wished she could do something, anything, to get through to the Buffy she used to know.

"Hey, Buffy, can you hand me that book on the shelf behind you? The one with the funny writing on the spine?"

Buffy turned and scanned the shelf. "Uhhh … Will, these all have funny writing."

Buffy selected a book and pulled it down. The funny-looking writing on the spine was deep red, almost invisible against the black leather cover. No writing appeared on the front, only an imprinted symbol in the same deep red. She held up the massive book with both hands where Willow could see.

"This one?"

"No, the smaller one next to it."

Buffy set the black book on the round table in front of the bookshelf, then pulled out a slim, brown volume covered in some sort of reptile skin. Buffy wasn't sure, but the book felt like it moved beneath her fingers as she handed it over to Giles.

"Most certainly we can hold it for you," Giles said into the receiver as he took the *Karatouch Tome* from Buffy, then hung up the phone and scribbled on a sticky note.

"Isn't that one of those living books?" Tara asked.

"Yes, the reptilian one." Giles smoothed the note across the cover of the *Karatouch Tome* and slipped the book onto a shelf behind the counter.

"Ewwwww, touching it gives me the willies." Willow gave Tara a look and smiled. She knew she didn't have to say what she was thinking. But she said it anyway. "Not a big fan of reptiles—especially those snakes."

Giles knew what Willow was thinking, too, and the reference didn't make him happy. He frowned, then grabbed a feather duster and headed for the stairs to the second floor. He scowled at Willow as he walked by, but he didn't say a word.

Tara swallowed hard, then looked over at Buffy, noticing she was staring off into the distance. "Ah … Buffy? Are you okay?"

"Huh?" Buffy snapped out of it. "Nothing. I'm fine. Thinking about Dawn—I think she's been smoking."

"Our little Dawn's turning into a *bad* girl," Willow said, smiling a little too broadly for Buffy's taste.

"I'm thinking this is a little more serious." Buffy's face turned sour.

"We know," Tara said, half-smirking behind her hand, "but the image of Dawn smoking is just so … "

"You'd better be thinking 'horrifying,'" Buffy said.

Willow tried to regain her composure. "We're sorry, Buffy. It's just that we've spent a lot of time with Dawn while you were … ummm, anyway, the stuff she's doing, it's just her acting her age."

Buffy started for the door. "Well, yeah, maybe it was better that way. You guys looking over Dawn. Me, dead."

Willow stopped laughing. Both she and Tara stared slack-jawed at Buffy, fear and hurt in their eyes. A wave of nausea washed over Buffy as she realized what she'd said. She felt sick, like she'd taken a punch to the stomach. She turned back to her friends.

"I … I … didn't mean that the way it sounded. I just meant …"

"Buffy, you need to get back into the swing of things. You know, hanging out with people again, like going back to school."

"Tried that, Will. Didn't take, remember?"

"Or … maybe you need to get a job … or something … to occupy your time," Tara said.

"Hello, I have a job. Slaying vampires. Sure, the hours suck and the pay's terrible which really blows, because I need to find a way to pay these bills that just keep coming. Next thing you know I'll resort to working at a fast-food place. But not now." Buffy walked back over to the table where Tara sat and slumped down into a chair.

Willow came up and put her hands on Buffy's shoulders, giving her a reassuring squeeze. "Don't worry, Buffy. You'll be back to feeling normal soon, I just know it. And don't worry about Dawn. I don't think she's taken up smoking. If anything, she's just experimenting … you know, like Tara said, acting her age. She's a good kid, but she's stubborn—a lot like another Summers I know."

Buffy casually flipped open the oversized book that was on the table in front of her. Willow sat down between her and Tara.

Willow said, "Hey, is this the book you pulled off the shelf?"

"Yeah. Weird one, huh? Looks right up your alley with spells and stuff."

"It looks right up evil alley," Tara said. "You know how some books can creep you out … even if they're not alive? Well, that book—"

"Interesting. I haven't seen this before." Willow pulled the book closer and flipped through a few pages herself. "*The Book of Tears*. I've never even *heard* of it."

"Sounds kinda evil." Tara closed her textbook and slipped it into her backpack.

"No, no, it's not evil, it seems way cool—if this first spell is any indication. I've been looking for something like this. Wow, you can find the strangest things on the Magic Box's shelves, can't you?"

The bell above the front door jingled, and the trio turned to see Xander and Anya enter the shop.

"Hey, you two. How did the whole registering thing go?" Tara asked.

"It was great. We are going to be getting some really fantastic kitchenware," Anya said, spreading her arms wide. "But Xander didn't seem too happy with the idea of the spring-form pan."

"What's a spring-form pan?" Buffy asked.

"Apparently, it's for cute little cakes and tortes." A satisfied smile crept its way onto Xander's face, then just as quickly slipped away as he sensed the unease in the room. "Hey, no cute little cakes at *this* party. Why so glum, chums?"

"I'm sorry." Buffy leaned back in her chair. "It's my fault. I'm trying to motivate, but it's hard to get back into real life after, well, you know. Everything I do—big struggle."

Willow closed the book and tucked it under her arm. "Well, Tara, *we'd* better motivate, or we'll be late to class."

"I'll drive you guys." Xander pulled his keys out of his pocket and spun them around his finger like they were a six-shooter. "I've gotta stop in at work for at least a little bit this afternoon, and the campus is on my way."

"Wait just a minute!" Anya pointed at *The Book of Tears* under Willow's arm. "Did Giles say you could take that?"

Willow turned toward Anya and held up the book. "This? Don't worry, I'll just borrow it for a little while. I'll bring it back."

Anya shouted after her: "This isn't the library! You just can't take my merchandise without paying for it! Oh! I wish Giles would do something about this!"

Anya gritted her teeth and made her hands into tiny fists as she watched Willow and Tara leave with Xander. Then she looked around the shop. "Where *is* Giles, anyway?"

"Upstairs." Buffy pointed at the steps. "Dusting, I think."

Anya looked up at the shelves of books just peeking over the balcony railing. "Why is he never around when I need him around and always around when I don't want him around?"

Buffy sighed. "Look, I'd better get going, too. I've got to get some stuff done around the house before Dawn comes home from school."

"Buffy, wait." Anya stretched out an arm toward Buffy. "I have something that might be able to help you."

"*You* have something that will help *me?*"

"Yes, small gifts help cheer people up, right? So I'll give you—" She looked around the display case. "—The Amulet of Arathor. It came in yesterday. You know, gotta keep turning the stock." Anya opened a drawer behind the counter and pulled out a simple silver chain, set with a single red gem. She held it up and the light jumped and danced off the stone's facets with a hypnotic brilliance.

"It's beautiful, Anya. What's it do?" Buffy took the necklace from Anya and put it around her neck.

"Whenever you feel tired or run down, just give the amulet a little rub, and, presto! You're back in business. It's a good-luck charm."

"Sort of like a magic rabbit's foot?"

"Rabbits are creepy and evil and about as likely to bring good luck as …"

Buffy tuned her out. She rubbed the amulet, and the silence that filled the space all around her, for just a moment, felt good.

SNEAKING A TASTE

BLOOD FILLED HIS MOUTH. The vampire drank from the pretty college girl's neck. The girl had screamed, screamed for God and Mommy. Now her lips were turning blue, and her eyes were turning white. The blood kept coming, spraying from her neck like warm, wet, dragon's fire.

When it stopped, he dropped the body. He stepped over it like a disposed candy wrapper. Still hungry, he moved into the shadows of night.

Spike saw him slip around a row of Dumpsters that stood behind a campus diner. He thought for a moment about not following him, letting him go. What the hell did he care, really?

But it wasn't any kind of moral dilemma that stopped Spike. It was the thought of blood, the thought of drinking blood from a girl's neck. It made all the difference. He flashed back to times when he and Drusilla fed with the abandon of aristocrats. Killing just for a taste. No longer about feeding or sustenance. All about the rush you get when blood fills your mouth, and it comes so fast you have to fight back the gag reflex and just drink. And you can't stop or it'll run down your chin. Then you find you're not drinking so much as lapping up the sticky red liquor like a thirsty dog in front of a water bowl.

A hand on Spike's shoulder made him spin around quickly. He shook the nostalgic cobwebs from his mind. Even if it was because of some chip the military put in his head that prevented him from harming humans, he knew he was done with feeding. Resist the temptation. Just forget about it. Concentrate on the black-skinned vampire now standing in front of him.

"It's like this—if you're gonna follow me, get your ass to followin'. I ain't got all night, player."

"Parnassus?" Spike asked. "Parnassus Jones? Well, I'll be damned."

"Damned you may very well be, brother. Damned indeed." Parnassus laughed. "How long's it been, Spike? Thirty years? Forty?"

"Lost count, mate. But looks as though you lost your way. What brings you to Sunnydale?"

"Blood. Power. Pursuit of the ultimate high. Same ol', same ol'."

"Unfortunately you picked the town with the Slayer in it."

"The low down in the downtown said the Slayer was dead, six feet in the ground. Makes the alley ripe for this cat, what I thought." Parnassus laughed again, this time sounding slow and choppy like a broken airplane propeller.

His whole life, before and after the turning, had been slow and choppy. Parnassus—his Christian name lost in time and legend—was born in Mississippi in the mid-1800s, by all rights a miserable time and place to be a black man in America. His parents joined a wagon train as laborers to make the move out West for the Gold Rush when he was just a kid, taking him along to start a new life. He barely made it across the country alive. His mother didn't, the trip too hard and too long. His father died a bitter, angry man a few years after their arrival in San Francisco.

Parnassus kicked around California for a while, doing odd jobs, eventually signing up with Central Pacific Railroad when he was barely working age, laying track for the western half of the transcontinental railroad. The forced labor conditions on the rail line didn't suit him, and he decided to get the hell out of the United States. So he traded his strong back for passage on a ship bound for Greece.

Spike laughed at Parnassus's comment about the Slayer. "Out of touch with everybody but yourself, as usual. She's back, you know."

"So I've heard."

"Yep. Good as new." Spike lit a cigarette. "Hell, even a bit cuter, if you like 'em dangerous and deadly."

"No matter—my plan don't involve her. Long as I gots a city full of blood drinkers, I'm in business."

"You're not afraid she'll stop you?"

"Not if she doesn't know about me. Not like I'm gonna go around and blow things up. Or do something stupid like try to bring about the end of the world."

"That stuff's for amateurs, eh?"

"Or vamps that got a dust wish. Damn, I ain't playin' that game."

Spike doubted the subtlety of this so-called plan. He knew Parnassus's history, and it was anything but low key. On the ship he took to Greece, Parnassus had met a distinguished gentleman named Kharílaos, who had offered to share his quarters and teach him the ways of the world. He started by introducing him to the taste of blood. It was Parnassus's first high, as he drank from Kharílaos's arm, still feeling the ecstasy of Kharílaos's bite.

Sometime later he re-christened himself Parnassus Jones in a perverted baptism of young girls' blood.

Spike met him much later during a couple lazy years in Tangiers, feeding on hapless expatriates and wandering souls no one would miss. Parnassus wasn't quick or overly aggressive, but he proved to be more bloodthirsty and sadistic in his killing than even Spike.

"Remember Tangiers, Spike? Damn, you and me knew how to rush the action. But I found me a much bigger rush, and I'm laying it down in the S.D."

Spike licked his lips. His cigarette spent, he threw it to the ground. "It involve blood?"

"Not just blood, my brother. I'm talkin' primo juice my players pay buck for."

"Lots of bucks?"

Parnassus clapped him on the back. "Folks shoulda called you William the Money 'stead of William the Bloody! Let me tell you 'bout the score."

He leaned in toward Spike, closer than Spike would have liked. Spike flinched and tried to take a step back, but Parnassus grabbed him by the shoulder, leaned in closer, and whispered: "I got something called Jube—it don't do dick when brothers sniff it or lick it, but humans are all Lucy in the Sky with Diamonds." He laughed at his own falsetto. "But here's the joint—feed on this meat when they're all crunched in the head, and it'll tickle your toes and wiggle your willie like you never been done."

Spike made his hands into fists so that his slight trembling wouldn't show. "Bollocks, Jones, I've tasted Slayer blood—it doesn't get better than that."

"So you think. I'm tellin' you, Jube makes Slayer blood taste like milk."

Spike found himself frustrated by this conversation, more so than he should have been. He turned to leave as he pulled another smoke from an almost empty pack. "Sounds too rich for me. I'll stick to feeding off regular veins," he lied.

"Blondie, I ain't chargin' you, I'm cuttin' you in. Tell you what—bring all your friends 'round to one of my soirees. More they spend, more I cut you in, aight? I'm not passin' this deal on to everyone—but you and me, we used to be tight. And I'm all about gettin' the word out on this damage."

Spike paused. "When and where?"

"I'm movin' in on a party scene, something the boys and girls 'round here likes to call The Faint. We got music and dancin' and—"

"All right, what gives? Doesn't sound like your style. Fact, sounds an awful lot like someone else I remember. You're still hanging out with that Velatti girl, aren't you?"

"Funny you should say that." Parnassus wasn't laughing. "I give the girl the high hat years ago. Then bam, outta the blue 'bout a month ago, she's all puppy-dogging me, playin' like a groupie."

"You're a regular rock star, Parnassus Jones," Spike said.

"Damn, Blondie, I just keeps her around 'cause she's easy on the eyes is all. You know what I'm sayin'. How's that Drusilla girl of yours?"

Spike's frustration returned. He wondered how much Parnassus was playing him.

"Dru's gone."

"Good." Parnassus laughed loud, right in his face. "Never liked that funny-talkin' bitch."

A foul wind blew up from the Dumpster. Spike was done with this conversation. So was Parnassus.

"Faint. Just remember it, player. And spread the word for your ol' friend, Parnassus."

† † †

Buffy rubbed the Amulet of Arathor in her hand. She had just dusted a pair of loser vamps trolling campus. It felt good. She felt good. Somehow touching the red stone made the issues with her sister drift away.

She had already done a sweep of campus, the cemetery, and now she was feeling ready for more, even though it was still early. The streets near the Bronze were a good bet—the dark alleys around the nightclub had a large population of homeless and other street life. Plus plenty of good places for vampires to nest.

Patrolling Sunnydale for vampires could really feel like a chore sometimes. She'd been doing the rounds with Spike a lot lately. She felt drawn to him, although she knew he was no good for her. Like the way that scratching an itch only makes you more itchy. But tonight she was enjoying being by herself. It felt more like a hunt. She could taste the night air. And if she moved slowly enough, she could smell the nearness of vampires.

Turning a corner, she saw a pretty platinum blonde wearing the greatest miniskirt she'd seen in the longest time. This girl had two leather-clad boys, one wrapped around each arm. They were like dance-club scarecrows—high leather boots; tight black shirts; long, messy, spiked hair. She knew right away, all three were vampires.

"Excuse me, miss," Buffy said, moving closer. "Before I kick your ass, you *must* tell me where you got that skirt."

The two boys turned on their vamp faces. The girl put her hands on her hips and just smiled, all sweet and sexy.

"I'd tell you, honey, but then I'd have to kill you." Her brow wrinkled up, and fangs showed behind her painted lips. "Come to think of it, I'm going to have to kill you anyway. Boys?"

The pair of vamps ran at Buffy. She spun and kicked one of them right in the stomach. She jumped back, and when the other one ran past her, she slammed him on his back with both elbows. He went down. She pulled a stake out of her jacket and drove it into his back. Dust.

The girl grabbed her from behind. "Got ya!"

The vampire that Buffy had kicked charged at her like a high school football player, only 150 pounds lighter.

She pushed back against the girl's grasp and kicked the oncoming vamp again, this time with both feet square to the chest. Stupid vampires.

"At least tell me," Buffy said as she twisted around, breaking the hold, "does the skirt come in green? That black is so tired."

"Green?" She swiped at Buffy's face, missing. "Please. Not with your skin tone. You'd look positively dead. But maybe that suits you."

Buffy pivoted around and shoved her stake into the remaining boy vamp as he tried to charge her from behind. They never learn.

Buffy looked up, and the girl had swung again. This time she connected with a fist across Buffy's face, sending her stumbling back.

"Good thing you're an easy mark. This skirt may look good, but it's *hell* to fight in."

"Don't complain to me if you don't know how to fight *and* look good at the same time. It's sad, really." Buffy brushed her hand across the amulet around her throat and smiled.

Then she let the girl have it. A triple combination to her face and a strong kick to her kidney. But even though Buffy was quick with the stake, the girl was quicker. She was already up and running away.

"I can't believe you're running away! What's with you vamps? Don't tell me you're all finally starting to realize you can't beat me?" But the girl was already gone.

Buffy rubbed the amulet one more time. She breathed in a deep, heavy, satisfying breath.

"Amazing. Just amazing." Willow sat at her desk, eyes flitting back and forth across the pages of *The Book of Tears.*

Behind her, Tara lay on her bed, fingers clacking across the keys of her laptop. "You still reading that book?"

"Yes, it's amazing."

"So you've said. What makes it so amazing?"

"It opens my eyes to so much—so many things I've been doing wrong, well not *wrong*, really, just not completely right. It puts everything into perspective, makes casting a lot more clear. I can't wait for us to try some of these spells."

"You should see what they're saying about it on trismegistus.box.sk."

"The magicz site? Why are you messing with those amateurs?"

"Not messing, I thought I'd check out the buzz on this book. There seems to be some debate whether or not it really exists."

"Oh, it exists, all right. You can tell the so-called witches you're chatting with that."

"I did. They think it's a fake, and—argh!"

"What's wrong?"

"I'm trying to type and DorothyL keeps hitting me with IM after IM. She wants to trade this potion she made. Some witches just don't know when to stop."

Willow looked at Tara. "You know, you're really cute." She flashed Tara a knowing smile. Tara smiled back, a coy, seductive smile. They sat there, looking at each other and savoring the moment.

From down the hall, they heard Dawn yell, "I'm going to bed. Try to keep it down."

"Okay, Dawnie," Tara yelled back, then quieter: "Maybe we're being too loud."

"Maybe we can do something really quietly?" Willow smiled.

"Okay, but you've gotta put that book away."

"Sure, I can put the book away."

But even as Willow got under the covers, her mind stayed with the book and with magic.

All Dawn could think about during the whole day at school was sneaking out again tonight to go to Faint. And now, standing in the darkness of her room, the way she figured it, slipping by Willow and Tara would be cake, but the evening's big challenge would be getting past Giles. He was crashed out on the couch, where he'd been every night for the last couple of weeks, probably reading or something. And since the stairs let out right in full view of the living room, leaving out the front door was not an option.

But the fabulous Dawn Summers had a Plan B—the time-honored tradition of climbing out the bedroom window. Her hands shook a little as she unlocked the window and gave it a gentle tug. No luck; it felt jammed. She grabbed the handle with both hands, strained, and yanked up on the handle as hard as she could.

A sharp pop, then the window slammed wide open. Dawn froze and held her breath, hoping the sound wasn't that loud. Cool night air swirled around her as every creak of the house jolted her nerves. She listened for footsteps, body tensed, ready for a frantic jump back into bed.

After a few agonizing minutes, she decided she was in the clear. She took her shoes off, throwing them down to the lawn below. Fashion could wait for Faint; right now she needed the extra traction of bare feet.

The climb itself was easy, as long as she could scurry down quickly and avoid sticking out too much. She poked her head out the window and looked down. Well, it wasn't so much a climb as it was a drop. She slipped out the window as fast as she could. She held onto the window sill and, bare toes digging into the brickwork of the house, slowly lowered herself until her body was fully extended. She looked down again. Hanging from the window like this, it wasn't all that far of a drop, really.

Plop. She hit the ground and rolled, like the girls did in *Charlie's Angels*, ignoring the slight twinge in her right ankle. She snapped up her shoes and was on her way. Just to be safe, she wouldn't put them on until she'd hooked up with Melinda at the end of the street. But right now she wasn't thinking about Melinda; she was thinking about Skeeter. She played through a variety of potential scenarios of what she would say to him and what he would say to her …

"Where do you think you're going?"

Dawn froze, caught cold halfway to the sidewalk, halfway to freedom. Buffy stood in front of her with crossed arms and a cross look.

"Ah, back to bed?" Dawn raised her voice at the end, hoping, somehow, to get out of this one.

No luck. Buffy spun her around and marched her back toward the house.

"Good guess."

THE BEST EXPERIENCE

Dawn swirled a final French fry in the messy mix of ketchup and mustard. She didn't feel like being in public today. All she really wanted to do was lay on her bed, put on some loud music, and pout.

 Sometimes a good pout really made her feel better. But she had stuff to do; tonight wasn't going to be like last night. No way. She popped the fry into her mouth and looked up at Melinda, sitting across from her. Melinda frowned as she made a sucking sound with her straw as it scraped the bottom of her empty milkshake.

"I still *cannot* believe you got busted last night. I mean, I waited there for like twenty minutes. I was so totally ready to go trancin'."

"Yeah, so you keep saying. I'm not thrilled about it either. I woulda been free and clear, too, if stuffy old Giles wasn't staked out on the couch."

"That bugs. What is *up* with that guy and your sister, anyway? I mean, it's like … weird."

Dawn wondered if she could get away with the truth: Oh, you see, my sister is the Vampire Slayer, fighting the good fight right here in Sunnydale, and Giles is her Watcher. Yeah, right. Like she wouldn't be the biggest joke of the whole school on Monday with a story like that.

"Summers? You okay?" Melinda gave her shake a little jiggle. Inside, the straw rattled against the paper cup.

Dawn needed a good story, and fast. She looked around the restaurant, feeling too much like one of those paramecia they studied in biology on Friday. Then she saw the crazy scene a few tables away and knew she had an out.

"Omigod. Melinda. Look over to my right. Dork, family of four, your seats are ready."

Melinda craned her neck to get a good look, then put both hands over her mouth to stifle a giggle. "Tourists. Can you *believe* they are videotaping their trip to In-N-Out Burger? Lame."

"So lame. Those two little boys, stuck with their parents. Such a burden of uncoolness."

"Not like us. No parents here." Dawn winced at her own words. No parents. No mom. Deadbeat dad. She hoped Melinda didn't bring that up.

"Right on. We're the new regime of hip. I mean, come on, tonight, for sure, we'll be at Faint. How cool is that?"

"As cool as it gets. And now that we hooked up with Skeeter, we are *so* in."

Melinda stuck her tongue out at Dawn, then said, "You *wish* you hooked up with Skeeter."

Dawn ignored her friend and got up to leave. "Let's go. I'm done hanging here."

"Dude, I'm with you. I think it's time to go to the place."

After they left the restaurant behind, they headed down the main drag, eventually turning the corner onto a less-busy side street. Dawn looked around to check that they were alone.

Melinda reached into her purse and pulled out a single sad-looking cigarette. "I only have one. Split it with you."

Dawn hesitated. "Cool. We should get more for the next time we go to the club."

Melinda lit up. "Oh yeah. No problem. If the guy at 7-Eleven won't sell them to us, we'll give some homeless guy money to buy them."

"Classic." Dawn puffed at the cigarette. She still hadn't quite got the hang of inhaling yet, and the smoke made her queasy. Still, she thought she could feel a little buzz going to her head.

"Do you think these flyers will be hard to find?" Dawn asked.

"Doubt it. They weren't yesterday. Skeeter said there's always a bunch of them listing the Faint location stacked under the free papers in the bin at the corner of Petrie Street and Espenson Way."

"It's not the best neighborhood. I can't believe you went without me yesterday."

"I wasn't the one stuck in the house. Now, chill. It's the middle of the afternoon, on a Saturday, even. What could possibly happen? All we gotta do is grab a slip of paper."

"All right, let's get there." Dawn handed the half-smoked cigarette back to Melinda.

"Are these guys great, or what?" Xander tapped his hand on top of the little table, keeping time as Stickshift Rocketship cranked through "Total Disaster" on the Bronze's small stage.

Tara nodded in agreement in rhythm to the music. "A little Bowie, a little Stones …"

"Early Stones," Xander said. "And a whole lot of attitude."

Anya walked up to the table carrying a basket of sourdough pretzels. "Look what they're selling here now."

"They sure are all with the menu." Willow took a pretzel from the basket. "So, how are the wedding plans going, Anya?"

"Great!" Anya placed the basket of pretzels on the table, and everyone snatched one up. "This weekend we've got a few places we'll be looking at for the reception, and then we get to choose the linens and the flowers and the—"

"So, how's that pretzel?" Xander asked, pointing at Buffy.

Anya put her hands on her hips and glared. "Xander!"

Buffy wrinkled her nose. "Ugh. Cold. Don't they know these things are supposed to be served hot?"

"With cheese." Tara said. "Lots of cheese."

"Let me." Willow gestured at the pretzel. "*Aufwaermen!*"

Willow's eyes glowed black for a brief second,

and the pretzel in Buffy's hand exploded with a shock of flame.

"Ouch!" Buffy dropped the pretzel, shaking her hand. "Uh, now it's maybe a little too hot."

"Ooopsie. Guess I overcooked it a bit."

Tara frowned. "Willow, I don't think it's a good idea to misuse magic like that."

"Come on Tara. It's not misuse. A flick of the wrist, nothing up my sleeve, and viola, eldritch energy making life easier."

"And is that what this *Book of Tears* is? Making life easier?"

"No, it's not."

"Willow, it's dangerous."

"Why are you always harping on me about this? I know what I'm doing!" Willow, pushed herself away from the table, and her chair fell backward and skittered onto the club's cramped dance floor.

"Willow!" Tara bolted from the table and tried to keep up with Willow.

Xander leaned back and put his hands up in front of him. "Yikes. Trouble in paradise for the good witches of the West Coast."

"Xander! You interrupted me back there. You interrupt me every time we talk about the wedding."

"Now's not the time to discuss this, Ahn."

"When, then? When is the time? It's *never* the time!" Anya covered her face and pushed through the crowd toward the door.

"I guess I'd better go after her." Xander looked at the stage as the band played the final notes of the tune; he frowned, then turned to look at Buffy.

Buffy shrugged. "Don't look at me. Buffy and relationships don't mix."

"Looks like I'm leaving, too." Xander snapped up his coat and started for the door. "Anya, wait!"

Buffy sat alone at her table, watching the backs of her friends, the silence once again taking hold, despite the applause filling the room. It all faded to a low throb in her head. She looked around and wondered why she bothered coming here. She didn't fit in anymore. No one knew what she was going through.

Then she saw Spike sitting at the bar.

✝   ✝   ✝

Skeeter loved watching the girls, most of them barely dressed, dance like possessed creatures. Some would shake, some would sway, but they all had that something in the way they moved. Most of them bought drugs from him. But Skeeter didn't think of them as his clients. No, he was their host, providing an experience for them—the best experience.

The experience he was currently trying to perfect came in a glowing water bottle. But high-school chemistry and a garage laboratory could only take you so far. He needed something more. It didn't matter that it was the most popular drug in Sunnydale's underground. Skeeter just happened to be a guy who liked to take things to the next level.

"Excuse me …" Even before he heard her voice, he could smell her sweet breath and feel it warm against his ear. "Can you come with me for a sec?"

"What? I can't hear you," he lied. Her short, choppy, platinum hair tickled his nose as he leaned into her.

She put her arm around him and licked her lips in his ear before she tried to yell over the loud blanket of music. "I want you to come. With me. If you're not. Too busy."

"Don't I get to know your name first?"

"I thought you knew all the DJs here. I'm shocked … and a bit hurt. I'm Velatti."

"I know." Skeeter smiled his best bedroom smile. "I just wanted to hear you say it."

She moved in even closer, her body tight against his—close enough that she didn't need to shout.

"So you like to play? Come with me, little player. I want you to meet someone who has the secret ingredient to jack your magical water bottles up to the next level."

As much as he didn't want to, he pulled away from her. He was shocked enough by what she said that he wanted to look in her eyes. They drew him back into her. He put his lips close to her ear.

"I can't believe it. I was *just* thinking about that. I mean, that *exact* thought."

"I know, Skeeter, honey. That's why you have to come with me."

He knew she was right. That's why he didn't bother to ask how she knew his name.

† † †

"Hey, Slayer. Buy you a pretzel?"

Buffy slouched into the seat next to Spike as if her whole body were a loud sigh. She ignored Spike's comment and just said, "Argh. Friends."

"Right." He looked up at her with a sideways glance while resting his elbows on the counter.

She adjusted herself on the stool, keeping her eyes lowered to the ground. "I know I was gone for a while—you know, being dead and all—but everyone's so different now."

"Tell me about it." Spike slapped his fist on the bar counter to emphasize his point. "I've worked alongside this cast of clowns for going on five months without you and—"

"I know, but is that long enough for all my friends to have changed so much?"

They sat for a moment without speaking. All around them couples mingled, the band continued to play. Buffy blew out a long breath. Spike sat up.

"Maybe it's not them that changed." He tapped her gently on the shoulder with the back of his hand. He avoided eye contact. "Remember the other night on patrol, we ran into a couple jokers talking about the boss?"

"Oh, don't tell me. You and this boss, old friends maybe?"

"Well, back in the day. Before things changed."

"What is it with you vampires? Do you *all* know each other?"

"They all knew the Big Bad, pet." Spike rolled his shoulders, adjusting his leather duster. "Anyway, this bloke, calls himself Parnassus Jones. The point is I know what he's doing in Sunnydale, and it ain't selling bibles door to door."

Buffy could feel that silence rising up around her like steam from a sewer grate. Another monster come to Sunnydale looking for trouble; another disaster she would have to face and conquer. Everything different. Nothing changed.

"I'll find him," she said. "Or he'll find me. That's how this works."

"Cooled down a bit since you clocked me one in the face, I see." He curled up his lips, then turned serious. "Buffy, I know … I know coming back has been hard. Hell, I'd like to say I even know what it's like. But if there's anything I can do, I mean—"

She stood up. The stone of the amulet draped around her neck felt warm. She closed a fist over it, and she could feel this longing, a struggle to find the answer to some question she couldn't even remember. Maybe this Parnassus was the key. Something had to be.

"Spike. Let's go."

Velatti led the way through the oblivious throng, trailing Skeeter behind her like a balloon. "Come on. It's just through this door."

The music faded to a distant pulse as they entered a spartan room that seemed like some sort of makeshift office. A simple chair, a plain folding table set up as a desk, and not much else. The scent of patchouli mixed with the wooden smell of the warehouse, the reality behind the façade of decadence.

Skeeter felt an instant familiarity with the black man reclining in the chair behind the table. Maybe it was the drugged-up and oh-so-sexy goth babe who reclined at the man's legs, her arms draped over his thigh, her eyes dreamily fixed on nothing at all. Maybe it was the man's threads that spoke to Skeeter. Whatever it was, Skeeter knew they were cut from the same cloth. The man was pure cool.

"Word on the street says you is the candy man, little player, and that all the boys and girls want your sweets."

Skeeter puffed up his chest. "Yeah, Skeeter's known for the high-Q."

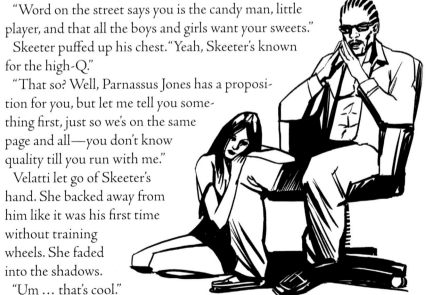

"That so? Well, Parnassus Jones has a proposition for you, but let me tell you something first, just so we's on the same page and all—you don't know quality till you run with me."

Velatti let go of Skeeter's hand. She backed away from him like it was his first time without training wheels. She faded into the shadows.

"Um ... that's cool."

Parnassus laughed at Skeeter's nervousness as he stroked the head of the girl on his lap like a pet. He slid an ornate wooden box across the table and gestured for Skeeter to open it.

Skeeter swallowed hard and stepped forward, reaching out to open the box. Now he could see that the top was carved with an image of a snake crawling out of the hollow eye sockets of a human skull. "What is it?"

"Let me tell you a second something, Shorty. You work for me, you don't ask the questions. You do what you're told. We straight on that?"

Skeeter looked into Parnassus's hard, black eyes. He could see the man was stone cold. Skeeter felt the sweat start to stream out from under his arms and run down the sides of his body. He wanted to know if Velatti was still there, but he didn't dare look over his shoulder. He nodded and lifted the lid on the box.

The box was filled with a fine, black powder. Skeeter thought it might be opium. He sniffed, but he'd never smelled anything like it before. Earthy and pungent, yet sweet. He wanted to get closer, put his nose right in it, bury himself in it, but Parnassus's voice brought him back down.

"Now what we want you to do, is keep on doing what you do, but instead of handing out your usual mix, we switch it up with this. You down?"

"I don't know, man, I got a rep ..."

Skeeter stopped talking when Parnassus stood up, his upper lip curled in a snarl. Parnassus shoved the girl off his leg, and she slumped to the floor, a giddy heap of flesh. Parnassus leaned over, put both palms flat on his desk, and put his face real close to Skeeter's.

"Seeing as how this is our first sit-down and all, I'm gonna cut you some slack. But you be questioning me in the future, this relationship be over real quick."

Skeeter nodded. He watched Parnassus dip his index finger into the black powder. Parnassus grabbed Skeeter by the back of the neck and pulled him close.

"You're gonna dig this." Parnassus nodded at the girl on the floor. She was squirming like a snake, writhing to some song only she could hear. "She sure did."

Parnassus slipped his finger between Skeeter's lips and rubbed the powder across Skeeter's teeth. Skeeter's tongue flicked out, licking the powder. A shock ran through Skeeter's body; he felt like he'd been hooked up to a car battery. His body jittered and danced as he stumbled backward into the door. He could barely keep his legs under him.

"Ohhhhhh, yeah. Totally Q."

"So, you in?"

"Yeah, I'm in."

Parnassus clapped the lid of the box shut and handed it over to Skeeter.

"Good. We start tomorrow. Now get outta here."

Skeeter nodded and felt Velatti's hand settle gently on his shoulder.

She steered him toward the door and back into the safety of excess.

Parnassus watched the heavy steel door slide shut as he slipped back into his chair. The music pounded out in the background. He tried not to listen to it as much as *feel* it. He wanted it to fuel his imagination, the same way Velatti used to. Seemed like a lifetime ago.

If he thought hard, he could remember that time when he could almost forego blood just to be by her side. A time when his sharp teeth first pierced her smooth, milky skin. A time when her blood had tasted so sweet, so pure, so innocent. Foolish, he knew now.

Eventually, like most diversions, she got boring. So when the Sedios demon offered him a deal—Velatti in exchange for some Essence of Execration—he took it. He remembered that stuff; it had kept him riding high for months.

But that was many lifetimes ago. He didn't think twice when Velatti had returned to him a few weeks ago. They always come back. But now he had even greater desires.

Parnassus turned his eyes to this other girl, still writhing on the floor in some macabre dance. She rolled onto her back, permanent grin etched on her face. "I … I can't feel my tongue." She looked so happy.

Parnassus knew that the drug destroyed her inhibitions and made her open to any suggestions. Sure he could sink his teeth into her and drink until he couldn't feel *his* tongue. But how much fun would *that* be? He'd rather hurt her—maybe even make her hurt herself—and make his high last. Last all night long. He stood up, stripping off his shirt.

Time to get busy.

VISIONS

As soon as she reached the house, Willow grabbed *The Book of Tears* and ran right back out before Tara could catch up with her. She hugged the oversized book as if it were a teddy bear as she headed toward the dark privacy of an overgrown vacant lot she knew of. No one would bother her there.

When she reached the entrance to the lot, she stepped around an old, homeless guy camped out next to the fence. The withered man looked up and smiled as he reached out and asked for change. He hoped to appeal to this girl's sense of charity or even pity; he didn't care which, as long as it meant a few coins in his pocket. Willow looked down and saw a broken smile of grime-blackened teeth. She sighed. A small part of her wanted to help the man, but the rest of her burned with the desire to make magic. She ignored him and went inside the graveyard, looking for the right spot.

She stopped at one of the buildings that bordered the lot. She touched the cool brick wall, hoping to draw in at least a little of its strength, watching its shadow stretch across the lot. She sat down on the cool grass in front of the building, surrounded by darkness, and placed the book across her lap.

Her bottom lip quivered when she thought about how difficult everything had been recently. Her hand went up to her eyes, and she tried to snap out of it, calm herself, get control of the situation. She tried to remember when it was she first found herself interested in magic, first showed strength in the discipline. But it became harder to focus on those thoughts as her fingers caressed the leather binding of *The Book of Tears*, and she was drawn into the comfort of now.

She liked magic. She was good at it. She liked the book. She understood its message. She was ready. Definitely.

She opened the cover and said with small, confident disdain: "*Ignis.*"

Candles rose up from the ground, and a thin trail of salt formed a pentagram around her. Behind her, the building now looked to be made of tiny bones, as if she could see the skeleton of architecture.

Willow was no rookie when it came to alternate dimensions. The rush she felt, even from the anticipation, put her in pure comfort. *The Book of Tears* contained a treatise on suffering. It told of a great dimension of ecstasy beyond pain, regret, and tears. Endure the journey, enjoy the destination. Simple.

She closed her eyes and began a slow, rhythmic breathing as she expanded her awareness, searching for essences of energy, intangible to any who didn't know how to find it, that she could tap into and manipulate. Then something, a presence, slipped into her zone. Anger flared hot in her mind, and she felt the candles around her blaze brighter. Her friends had grown critical of her use of magic. Why couldn't they understand that she was making things *better*? She struggled with her anger, a powerful emotion that too often caused miscasts. She'd had her share of those in the past, but she couldn't afford that anymore.

A deep breath, and she opened her eyes to see a figure walking out from behind the edge of the building. Thankfully, it wasn't any of her friends. The old man she had seen at the entrance stumbled up to her and dropped a plastic bag, riddled with rips and tears, at his feet. The clank of empty aluminum cans echoed in the cold night air.

The man had sat there in the dark, watching Willow begin the ceremony. He'd read the emotions that played across her face when she'd looked at him a few moments ago, and he knew she was the type who wanted to help. Maybe, just maybe, all she needed was to be asked again. He had pulled himself out of his bed of cardboard and newspaper, bringing his treasures with him, and shuffled over to the girl.

Willow looked up at the man's outstretched hand and smiled, then flipped through the pages of the book, toward the back. Her whole face carried the warmth of her smile.

Her eyes went black.

† † †

Skeeter followed Velatti back to the main action of the rave, his head bopping in time to the new samples from DJ Z-Trip that boomed from the monster-sized speakers.

"Hey, Velatti." Skeeter figured she couldn't hear him too well over the music, so he grabbed her arm at the elbow and gave a little tug. He jerked his hand away quick, startled. Her skin was ice cold.

Velatti whirled quickly, eyes narrow and cold. They softened a little when she saw Skeeter standing there, and she stroked her long, painted nails down one side of his face. She touched him so lightly that a little tickle started up just below his cheekbone and rippled across his jaw. A sort of warm buzzing started up in his guts and spread throughout his whole body. This girl did it for him, and she sure seemed to dig him. He wished they were alone.

"Yes?"

"Well, um, I was wondering that since now we're in business together, if you maybe wanted to grab some dessert over at this Greek diner I know. I mean, they've got great bearclaws and this awesome raspberry dessert they call—"

Vellati leaned forward and put a slender index finger to Skeeter's lips. "Shhhhh. That's very sweet of you, Skeeter, but I have different … desires."

"Oh, yeah? Hey, that's cool. We're all into different things."

"Oh, yes. Some *very* different … and some very much the same."

Willow uttered the last word of the spell and gestured at the man who stood in front of her. He cocked his head like a puppy, taking a few steps away from Willow and the pentagram.

Without warning, the sky opened up like a wound, and a thick bolt of lightning reached down like the arm of a surgeon. Fingers of electricity grabbed the homeless man and held him suspended a few feet off the ground, a rag doll strung up by high-tension wires. The energy lit up the night and seared a bright scar of light across Willow's eyes. She laughed, admiring her own power and the pure beauty of the light. She hadn't quite expected the reaction to be so violent, but change is often brought about by fierce energies.

The light vanished as rapidly as it had appeared, plunging the vacant lot into darkness; even the pentagram had gone out. Willow closed her eyes, and she could still see the beautiful blazing light imprinted on her vision.

The homeless man dropped to the ground in a tangle of bones and flesh. For a moment, Willow held her breath, afraid the man was dead. Then he groaned, rolled over, let out a shuddering breath, and looked up into Willow's face. He had tears in his eyes and the joy of oblivion on his face.

"Happiness is a warm fun thunder blunder mother may eyes wide hope and tears tears tears …"

His body glowed from the magical light still surrounding Willow, but slowly it extinguished as he drifted away into the night.

Her face turned sour with the horror of realization. "Oh my God. What … what *is* this? Did *I* really make that happen?"

She closed her eyes and felt the after-effects of the magic run through her veins. Something seemed wrong somehow, but the sensation that went from the base of her skull down to her fingertips felt so good.

Unmoving, peering into the blackness, she listened to the unnatural silence. The soft grass in front of her had been scorched black, and *The Book of Tears* lay shut in her lap. She hadn't remembered closing it.

She caressed the book again, this time with fascinated repulsion.

"Next time. Next time will be different."

When Buffy saw the lightning in the sky, it was as if the amulet around her neck had answered her request. She was looking for something, any-thing—a key, a connection, an end to the silence. As she held the amulet tighter, she knew the silence had been lifted.

"Spike, what … did you see that?"

"Yeah, me and the rest of Sunnydale. Now what I want to know is a little more of the who and the why. Wasn't an act of nature givin' us that show."

It was so clear. Obvious, really.

She turned toward Spike and nodded her head in earnest. "Thank you, Spike. Thank you for everything. I won't be needing your services anymore."

"Ah … services? Not catching your drift, Slayer."

It was as if a clear voice had sounded through the wet cotton that had anesthetized her life recently. She could hear the decision being made for her. Loud and clear.

"I'm the Chosen One. The Vampire Slayer. I slay vampires. Me."

"Right, you slay *bad* vampires." Spike jabbed a finger at the side of his head. "Vampires without chips in their heads. Just so we're still on the same page here."

Giles had been trying to get her to stand alone. Fine. It always boiled down to *her* problems, *her* challenges, *her* destiny. Her, her, her. So here was the answer: it must be all about her. No complications, nobody else. She rubbed the amulet, and she felt good.

She bounced a cheerleader smile from cheek to cheek, then flicked her hair over her shoulder. "I've got a couple things to do before I hit the ol' hay. Busy-busy-busy me. Slay-slay-slay! See ya, Spike!"

He watched her trip along her merry way. It was a couple minutes before he closed his slack-jawed mouth, but it was in no time at all that he realized that tonight's crack of lightning had opened up some serious trouble.

Parnassus left the girl's bloodless body in the office. He'd watched her gasp and struggle to breathe her last few breaths as he waited for his high to take hold. He'd sat a moment, unmoving, and watched her pale face lose what little color it had left, until he could feel a nice mellow buzz start to rise up in the back of his brain. It would be a good ride tonight.

His favorite way to ride out a high these days was to crash out on the roof of some abandoned building. He usually didn't have much of a view of Sunnydale, but that didn't matter. Parnassus could see the city clear in his mind, how it would soon belong to him.

Parnassus raised his head to the sky. A beautiful cloudless sky on a blissfully quiet night. He watched the stars twinkle and dance above him as he fell to his knees, hypnotized by the distant points of light. He held his arms up high, over his head, and tried to pluck the stars from the sky one by one.

Then a fractured cord of lightning ripped through the darkness.

For a moment he thought he was blinded. He closed his eyes and watched the brightly burning after-image dance on the inside of his eyelids. He spread his arms wide and waited for the rain. But it wasn't rain that fell down on him. In fact, he was sure it felt like the soft, loving touch of fingertips.

Then, when he heard her voice, he knew that he was in love.

Skeeter slipped through the back door and into the dark alley behind the warehouse. He stopped, looked up at the slivered moon, and let the cool night air kiss the sweat from his skin. Inside, the rave was in full swing. He had run out of juice; everybody was high.

He'd been drinking plain water all night, sipping just enough of his own stuff to take the edge off. He needed to be relaxed when he dealt with the skanky teases that begged a high off him. Sure, he'd trade his goods for cheap moments of false intimacy in dirty bathrooms, but none of those sluts ever did much to inspire him. He needed a girl with cool, class, control.

A girl like Velatti.

The one thing about his stuff, though, it worked the bladder up real fast. He wondered if this new drug, Parnassus's mysterious black powder that he called Jube, would do the same thing. He stopped and faced the wall, his left hand absently picking at the brickwork. He had no idea what this new drug even was. A pang of guilt ran through him, but it didn't last long. He was getting in with Parnassus. He was moving up. And, well, his current product wasn't exactly FDA approved.

He leaned toward the wall, holding himself up with his left arm. He could feel the heavy bass thud through the brick and into his body as he struggled with his zipper. He stopped struggling when he heard heavy grunting from around the corner of the building. He smiled and pushed himself away from the wall. A couple someones were getting their rocks off back here. Worth a look.

He crouched down close to the ground and peeked just enough of his head around the corner to see the girl-on-girl action down the alley.

Two girls, leaned against a Dumpster, veiled in shadows. He could really only see one of the girls—a skinny, sweaty waif with her back to him. All he could see of the other one was a pair of arms wrapped around her partner's body, and that she had her face buried in the skinny girl's neck. It looked like she was working on giving the king of all hickeys. She ground her pelvis against the skinny girl rhythmically, and her partner moaned and grunted, her head lolling back on her shoulders like her neck was made of rubber.

A long, hollow, raspy sound slipped out of the skinny girl's mouth, and her knees buckled. The other girl threw her head back, looking up at the sky, a silent scream on her lips. The skinny girl slipped from her partner's grip and crumpled to the ground. Blood spurted and bubbled from the fallen girl's neck, and when Skeeter looked back at the other one, he could see that blood covered her face and the tips of her platinum hair. It looked black in the dim moonlight. The hot girl smeared the blood across her lips and moaned in ecstasy. Then Skeeter recognized her.

Her head snapped down and looked right at Skeeter, again with those hard eyes.

Skeeter had seen some weird things in his time around raves. Overdoses, bad trips, and plenty of spilled blood when two stoned ravers decided to throw down. But this, this was more than his mind could process. He ran from the alley, forgetting about the rave, forgetting about his bladder, and, most of all, forgetting about Velatti.

PROBLEMS

"ANYA, WHY'D YOU HAVE TO DO THAT TO ME?"

Xander sat on the floor of his apartment, in the narrow hallway outside the bathroom door.

Anya's voice shouted back at him from the other side of the door. "How could *I* do that to *you*? Why is it always about *your* feelings? What about *me*? What about *my* feelings? How could you do that to me? I'm tired of being publicly humiliated."

"What? Come on, Ahn! You knew how much I wanted to see that band!"

"And you know how much getting married means to me! But that doesn't stop you from avoiding any kind of talk about it, or even keeping me from talking about it with your friends. It's like you don't want to be married to me."

The bathroom door banged open, startling Xander. He looked up and saw Anya standing there, red eyed. Still, he never thought he'd seen anyone quite so beautiful before. Xander got to his feet, wondering how to make this right. Sure, he loved Anya, much more than he could remember loving anyone.

But marriage? That's a big step. His parents were miserable in marriage. Would it be any different for him? Could he be happy with Anya?

"It's … it's not like that, Ahn."

Anya wrapped her arms around herself, like she was trying to comfort herself with a hug. "So you keep saying. But you never tell me what it *is* like."

Xander took a few steps toward Anya, pleading with his arms. "It's like … I don't *know* what it's like. I'm just scared, I guess. There, I said it. I'm just scared."

Anya brushed by Xander and walked toward the front door. "Well, Mr. Scared. You stay here and figure things out. Me, I'm going to the store."

"The store?" Xander looked at his watch. "But it's, like, three in the morning."

Anya turned around to face Xander. "Yes, well, sometimes, when I'm very upset, I like to go there at three in the morning. Or anytime of the morning, really, to touch the money. It's very soothing, feeling the money."

"I can't let you go there alone."

"Fine. But if you come with me, I just think it's fair to warn you that I'm not speaking to you." Anya spun on her heel, opened the door, and walked out into the hallway.

Xander sighed, grabbed his jacket, and followed Anya out the door.

"We have a problem."

Velatti stood, arms crossed, in front of Parnassus, who reclined, shirtless, in his chair. His high oozed off him like a viscous cloud. She hated talking to him when he was high.

Parnassus lifted his heavy-lidded eyes. "I don't like to be hearing that, baby."

"Yeah, well, I don't like to be saying it, but it happened. So let's deal."

"What happened?" Parnassus clumsily pawed at the card table, trying to pull himself up out of his slouch.

"Skeeter. He caught me feeding. He spooked."

"Ah, hell, girl!" Parnassus sat up in his chair. He felt his high start to melt away. It didn't make him happy.

"Calm down." Velatti held a hand out toward Parnassus, palm down, and patted the air. "It could have happened to anyone. So what do we do, kill him or turn him?"

"Man, this operation has gotta be low key. We can't afford some scared straight kid running around shootin' his mouth, and we can't afford to be schoolin' no new vampire."

"He can be an asset as a new born."

"No. No newbies. They're the worst—no control, eating everything they can get their fangs into. But, damn, we *need* that kid."

"We don't need him, specifically. We can get another one like him. He's not the only pusher in town."

"Don't tell me what we need and don't need. You don't know the plan—the plan's changed."

"The plan has changed?" Velatti leaned into the corner, intrigued by what seemed like an opportunity in Parnassus's wild shift in direction.

"Aight, here's what we do. You find him. See if he's gonna be trouble. After that, it's your call, either kill him or keep him on—as a human. But if you kill him, you gotta find a replacement."

"I was the one who found him in the first place." She began pacing. "And what's this about a changed plan?"

"Yeah, change in the weather. I've got bigger things on my mind. I had a vision. Naw, it was more of a visit—a visit from the Goddess of Tears."

Velatti stood and faced him, faking her anger. "No kidding. That happen when you were high?"

"I know what you're thinkin', and I don't need to hear it. I'm tellin' you, this here was the real deal. She's been forgotten and wants to be remembered. Can ya dig it? If I release her, bring her to this plane, she'll give me Sunnydale."

"Always like you to take the easy way out."

"What's that supposed to mean?"

Velatti looked down at Parnassus and sighed. He disgusted her these days. She remembered,

long ago, being turned on by his sexy self-assurance. Then he betrayed her, traded her away for a cheap high. Of course, he had no idea what would happen—did happen—to her at the hands of a Sedios demon, and that was the worst insult of all. Now all Velatti could see of him was a sweaty, strung out mess. Despite the disgust, she did feel a little sorry for him, but that wouldn't change what she had planned for Parnassus Jones.

"Nothing. It's not supposed to mean anything." She shifted the conversation. "You have any proof of this 'vision,' or do you plan on following your drug-addled gut?"

Parnassus grinned because he *did* have something, something that made it all very real. He held a metallic statuette, more like a chalice than a figure, in his hands.

"See? She gave me this device. Something to summon these dawgs called the Harvesters. They'll bring her here once I have what she wants."

Velatti rolled her eyes. "So, what's this Goddess of yours want in exchange? You already gave away your soul."

"Yeah, there ya go with the drama. No, this is a simple thing." Parnassus continued to caress the Harvester device.

"All we need is the tears of a virgin."

Tara's body was curled up tight in bed, facing away from the door. The sliver of light from the hallway cut across her head resting on the pillow. She didn't move.

Willow slipped through the barely opened bedroom door as quietly as she could. She didn't want to wake Tara, mainly because she didn't want another argument about the misuse of magic. She just wasn't up to it. The spell in the vacant lot took more out of her than she'd anticipated, and now every part of her screamed for bed. The grass of the lot had been a little wet from the just-formed dew, and Willow shivered as she stripped out of her clothes. But it wasn't the damp cold that got to her, it was the experience of the spell.

Willow stumbled around in the dark, trying to pull a pair of pajamas from the dresser drawer. She thought about casting a quick see-in-the-dark spell, but honestly didn't know if she had it in her.

She felt she'd tapped into a new level of power. Okay, so it didn't work *quite* the way she wanted it to—and now that she thought about it, she couldn't remember what the spell was *supposed* to do—but the homeless guy seemed happier. And that was the point, really.

Willow crept over to the bed and slipped between the sheets. She lay her head on the pillow and thought about the bright, beautiful bolt of lightning. She smiled and drifted off.

She fell asleep so fast that she didn't hear Tara quietly crying next to her.

ALTERED STATES

DAWN SANK INTO THE FOLDS OF THE COUCH, clutching the cordless phone to her ear. "I can't believe you gave me such a hard time about getting busted the night before, and last night *you* couldn't get out. At this rate, we're *never* gonna get back to Faint."

Melinda yakked out some excuse on the other end. Then after they laughed it off, she wanted to make plans for this evening. But Dawn wanted to dish on the current situation first.

"I'm telling you, girlfriend, it's like everything went *totally* whacko around here. Willow and Tara are giving each other the silent treatment ... Yeah, I *know* ... Xander and Anya—fighting. I mean, hello, they just got engaged! ... Yeah, *totally* ... Oh, and it gets worse ... Yeah, my sister."

"Dawn!" Buffy stormed into the room, her hands on her hips. "What are you doing?"

Dawn looked up at her from the couch. "Ah, I'm talking on the phone with ... um ... Melinda."

"Great! Teenagers talk on the phone all the time. You're a teenager. Super! Just stay in and do teenage stuff—good stuff, of course. I've got to run out, but I'll be right back! Bye!"

The front door slammed shut. Dawn watched through the curtain as her sister marched merrily down the street.

She rolled her eyes and returned to the phone. "Melinda? Yeah, about tonight, sneaking out of the house?" She giggled. "No problem."

† † †

Skeeter didn't feel good. He'd been up all night, sitting in the dark, comforting confines of his room, chain-smoking blunts to calm his nerves, all the while trying to make sense of what his eyes saw the night before. About the time the sun started coming over the horizon, he'd made up his mind. He had to talk to Velatti.

Skeeter, bloodshot eyes hidden behind a pair of Arnette sunglasses, stopped outside Vinyl Cabaret and peered through the front window, hoping he'd be able to see something beyond the black mesh shade that hung on the other side. He couldn't make out anything but vague movement. At least someone was inside.

He came to the Cabaret all the time to deliver flyers for raves, and in some dusty corner of his memory he remembered seeing Velatti hanging behind the counter some nights. He didn't know who she was then. Now he didn't know *what* she was. Well, he had a pretty good idea, but it was hard for him to admit it to himself.

He swallowed hard, pulled the door open, and entered the small record shop.

A loud techno beat hit his ears; Skeeter thought it might be House of Venus. Only a few people milled about the store's narrow aisles: DJ types, or wannabes, looking for fresh tunes to spin that night. A gothed-up girl Skeeter knew stood behind the counter, flipping through a copy of *Fortean Times*. She called herself Demonia or something silly like that. Skeeter walked over to her.

"Hey, D."

"Skeeter. What's up?"

"Well, ah, is Velatti around? I've seen her here sometimes, and I need to talk to her."

"Yeah, I heard the two of you were bizzed up. She's hanging out." Demonia waved at a door behind the counter. "Go on back, just down the hall."

"Thanks." Skeeter flipped the hinged counter up and went through the heavy steel door.

He entered a hallway and wrinkled up his nose. A dank, musty, earthy smell washed over him and got right under his skin. When the door slammed behind him, the only light in the place came from a single anemic-looking bulb hanging in the middle of the hall. Ahead of him he could see a short flight of steps going down. Skeeter slid his glasses up on top of his head and made his way down the steps. He didn't have far to go before the hall dead-ended at another door.

He paused, blew out a big breath, and knocked. The sound boomed in the tiny hallway.

"You may enter," a smooth, sexy voice said to him from the other side of the door. Even muffled, Velatti's voice got him hot.

Skeeter pushed the door open and walked into the room, the rubber soles of his Skechers squeaking on the painted cement floor. Velatti sat in a squat leather chair with her legs propped up on what looked to Skeeter like an antique coffee table. She wore a pair of skin tight, light blue polypropylene pants and a black T-shirt that showed off the ring through her bellybutton. A Zippo lighter, ashtray, and a red pack of cigarettes rested beside her feet. A cigarette dangled from her fingers, filling the room with the smell of cloves.

"So. You know my secret." Velatti dragged deeply on her cigarette. Skeeter could hear the cloves pop and crackle.

"Well, I'm not sure. But it's pretty freaky. I thought about it a lot."

"Did you now." Velatti blew out a plume of smoke. "And?"

"I ... ah ... I ... think you're a v-v-vampire."

Velatti arched an eyebrow. "Oh? Been reading Anne Rice?"

"You mean you're *not* a vampire? So what was all that—"

Velatti took another drag.

"Relax. You win the prize. We're *all* vampires
at the Cabaret." As she spoke, wisps of smoke
curled up out of her mouth like phantom
snakes.

Skeeter felt the skin on the back of his neck
start to itch. "But, doesn't sunlight, like, kill
vampires?"

"We keep it pretty shady in here."

"But ... how do you get in to, like, open
the store during the day and all?"

"That's a secret. And you only get one secret per visit. Now, what did you come to talk to me about?"

"Uhhh … Well, after last night … um, I sort of thought about it and, well …" Skeeter took a deep breath. He felt his heart pounding in his chest. He looked her right in the eyes.

"I want to be a vampire."

"I'm not sure I can do that, Tara. Frankly, I'm not sure there's *anything* I can do." Giles poured the last of his breakfast tea into his cup, then set the pot down on the kitchen table between them. He looked up at her. "I can brew some more if you'd like."

"No, thanks. I've already had some—I've been up for a while." Her eyes darted around the room. "Can't you just t-talk to her … one more time? Try to m-make her understand?"

Giles lifted the lid off the pot and looked inside at the wet leaves in the strainer. "Lord knows I've tried to get through to her. I don't think talking is the answer anymore. Willow is traversing with powerful magic that is bound to take its toll."

Tara stood up. "W-what can I do?"

"If you love her, you have to be willing to let her choose her path. And you have to trust that she'll find herself in all this madness." He stood up as well and took the teapot and cup over to the sink.

"Giles … d-do you think we did the right thing … b-bringing Buffy back?"

Giles stared down at the dirty dishes and couldn't turn to face Tara. He rinsed out his cup and placed it on the pile. When was the last time that Buffy washed the dishes? Since he stopped doing them for her a couple days ago, they just sat here in the dingy water. He tried to think of a proper answer to Tara's question, but instead of thinking about if the gang did the right thing by bringing Buffy back, he thought about if *he* were doing the right thing by staying here in Sunnydale.

"Well, I suppose that—"

Willow walked into the room. Still in her pajamas, she stretched her arms out in a big yawn.

Giles looked at his watch. "—I should get a start on my day."

The two witches didn't say anything back.

The room grew quiet, and Giles knew there was nothing left to say. Whether he was hanging around the house or hanging around the Magic Box, it was all the same in the end: he was just hanging around. As he left the room, he passed Tara and gave her shoulder a little squeeze. Normally he would tell someone that he would be gone for the whole day, in case someone were looking for him or needed him. But now he just drifted away.

The lack of sleep didn't seem to have much effect on Willow. If anything, she was still a little punchy from last night, like a barfly who wakes up drunk. Tara watched her pace back and forth from the toaster to the refrigerator. Willow had sliced herself a bagel, then went to the fridge to grab the cream cheese. The spread had looked a little green, so she'd pulled out the butter instead. Now she flitted back and forth like a loose pinball while she waited for the bagel to get toasted.

"Will, you're making me dizzy."

Willow looked up at Tara and started to snap a response, but quickly caught herself. She could feel the anger burning behind her eyes and wondered why this simple comment had made her angry. She felt on edge, and she wasn't sure why. She paused a moment as she checked her bagel, then looked back up at Tara. This time, she hoped, her eyes would be friendly.

"Sorry, a little amped up, I guess. Did you eat already? Can I get you something?"

"N-no, I'm not hungry. Well, maybe I'll have a piece of fruit or something."

Willow picked up an orange and brought it to her. After she set it on the table, she leaned over and kissed Tara on the forehead.

The bagel popped up. The *ding!* of the toaster made Tara jump a little. She realized how dry her mouth was.

After Willow poured herself a glass of juice, she sat down across from Tara.

They sat in silence.

Tara was rolling the orange in her hands, testing with her thumb for a good spot to dig into the peel. Her short fingernail couldn't find a start, so she bit into the rind. The acidic spray stung her nose, and then the peel came off easily in small chunks of orange flesh.

She looked up at Willow and took a deep breath. "I'm worried about Buffy."

"Weren't you the one who told *me* to give it time?"

"Yeah, b-but … this morning she was acting f-funny, and I thought with all the … m-magic going on in the last couple days—"

Willow scooted her chair away from the table. "This isn't about Buffy, is it?"

"Y-yes!" Tara brushed her hair behind her ear. "Just f-forget I mentioned it."

The orange lay forgotten, half-peeled and uneaten. Tara was about to leave when she heard Buffy come in through the front door.

"Hello, everyone!"

"You're up and at 'em early today. Earlier than you've been up in a while." Willow drank the last of her juice.

"New Buffy means new Buffy schedule. If evil doesn't rest, then I shouldn't either."

"Well, it is almost noon," Willow said. "Don't you think that evil is at least napping?"

Tara ignored Willow's quip. "What's this about a new Buffy?"

Buffy picked up the orange off the table and finished peeling it. "What can I say? I saw this lightning flash in the sky last night and *bam!* It all became clear to me."

Willow ran over and hugged her. "That's super!"

"I'm glad you think so." Buffy popped an orange section into her mouth.

The light shining into the kitchen grew brighter. Willow's face seemed to glow. She went to put her arm around her girlfriend. "We definitely think so. We knew it would just take time."

"Great! And, Willow …" Buffy's smile rose with sweetness. "Thanks for everything."

The expression on Willow's face melted into a happy kind of awe. Her bottom lip trembled a bit.

Buffy turned away from her. "Time to go! Got to keep moving, doing what I do."

Tara called after her: "Where are you going? You just got back in."

Before she could even finish her question, Buffy had gone.

"See, I told you there was nothing to worry about." Willow gave Tara a peck on the cheek. "Buffy is back to normal!"

Velatti tapped the ash from her cigarette onto the floor, then smiled up at Skeeter. "You say you've thought this over?"

"Yes." Skeeter shifted his feet. He couldn't get comfortable.

"Have you really?" Velatti flicked her cigarette against the far wall of the room and stood up. "Being a vampire means never seeing the sun rise ever again—"

"I don't see the sun much anyway."

Velatti laughed. "You'd be surprised how much you'll miss the sun. You'll be a creature of the night, your body inhabited by a demon. And, most of all, you'll be consumed by your desire for blood. Human blood. You have to kill and kill and kill just to stay alive. Do you like blood, Skeeter?"

Skeeter stood there, staring. He couldn't get his mouth to form any words. Half of him was thrilled to be here, alone in the same room as Velatti. The other half of him, frightened. Either way, the fever of curiosity ran through him; he couldn't leave if he wanted to.

Velatti walked over to Skeeter and put her hands on his shoulders. She looked into his eyes, smiled, then slipped his sunglasses down into place.

"What are you—"

"Quiet. No talking."

Velatti steered Skeeter over to the leather chair and gently pushed him down into it. She dropped to her knees in front of him and lay her arm across his chest. Skeeter longed to touch her smooth, white skin. With a quick thrust, Velatti pierced the flesh on the inside of her arm near the wrist with the sharp nail of her little finger. She pulled the nail up her arm toward the elbow, opening a long, deep cut. Blood welled up, fast and thick. She held the wound up to her face, licking and slurping. The blood flowed into her mouth and trickled down her chin.

She leaned in, holding Skeeter's head in her hands, and kissed him on the mouth, long, hard, and deep—just how he liked it. The taste of her blood filled his mouth. He reeled.

"Do you like blood, Skeeter?"

"Yes."

Velatti leaned back, resting her weight on her heels. She ran a finger around Skeeter's lips, now covered with blood. She leaned in, put her lips against his cheek, and whispered. "I need you to do a favor for me."

"Mmmmm. Okay."

"At the rave tonight, Parnassus needs a virgin. A girl."

Skeeter sat up a little and laughed. "A virgin at a Sunnydale rave? Good luck."

"Oh, they're there all right. I know you can find one. Use your senses, don't use your brain. Once you pick one, I need you to do something … something for me."

"Uh … okay. What is it?"

"Parnassus will be distracted by this virgin you give him." She took his head in her hands and held it out away from her, looking into his eyes. "And when he is, I need you to kill him."

"Kill … Parnassus …? How?"

"With this." Velatti reached down and picked something off the floor. She handed it to Skeeter. He turned it over in his hands, looking at it, disbelieving. A sharp, wooden stake.

"But …"

"Right through the heart. You do this for me, you'll get your wish. And then we'll *really* have some fun."

She kissed him again. Every nerve in Skeeter's body burned.

Xander rubbed his eyes. Sleeping at the Magic Box didn't do much for his conversational abilities. He blinked and stared at Buffy, trying to understand what she'd just told him.

"So when you say 'new Buffy,' do you mean new-and-improved Buffy or do you mean—"

"It's more like back-to-basics Buffy." Buffy held her arms wide and looked up at the ceiling as she explained it all to him again. She couldn't figure out what was so hard to understand. "A bolt of lightning. Everything so simple. You know, I'm the Vampire Slayer."

"I for one think it's about time." Anya came forward and gave Buffy a supportive punch to the shoulder. "We *were* concerned that you were broken in some way. I can say that … now that you're better."

Xander, who had crashed out at the main table in the center of the shop, raised his head from the books he was using as pillows. "I'm sure that 'broken' wasn't the exact word Anya was looking for." He stifled a yawn. "But we were concerned about you, Buff."

"That's sweet." Buffy moved about the store, picking things up, half-looking at them. She grabbed a delicate crystal wand and absent-mindedly waved it around, her mind elsewhere.

Anya took the wand from Buffy and placed it back on the display shelf. "Are you looking for Giles?"

"No. Why, is he looking for me? I'm really busy today and I could have missed him."

The phone rang. Bleary-eyed, Xander looked up again from the books. "Man, every time I hear that phone it's ringing."

"Maybe that's Giles," Anya said as she crossed the room to get the phone. "I'm surprised he's not here. He's been awfully silent for a non-silent silent partner."

Buffy rubbed her fingers together in a nervous gesture. "Okay, I've checked in at the Magic Box, because that's what a good Vampire Slayer should do. Now, I'm off."

"Xander, Willow's on the phone for you."

Dragging his feet, Xander made his way to the counter and picked up the phone. Willow's voice came across a little too loud and cheery. He held the phone away from his ear. "Yeah, she's right here … Buffy, hold on a sec."

Almost at the door, Buffy turned, her eyebrow impatiently arched.

"Okay, okay," Xander stumbled through the call. "I'll ask her."

Anya smiled, waiting to find out what the deal was. She looked up at Buffy, who was still standing by the exit, then she looked at Xander. He put the phone down and cracked his knuckles.

"I know it's been a long time since we've done this, but I have to agree with Willow. Today's a perfect day for it—being Sunday—and with Buffy feeling back to normal … oh, and let's not forget the serious slow down on the monster front—"

"Xander!" Anya glared at him. "What is it?"

"Movie night. Let's get the whole dang Scooby gang together and watch a flick or two. What d'ya think, Buff?"

"A great idea! We always had a good time on movie night. Let's all meet up at the house. I'll be there as soon as I finish up the stuff I already have planned."

Xander let his eyes roam around the shop. It was funny how much this place reminded him of the old high-school library, the home base of their early adventures. At the same time, it seemed so different, as if it were developing its own sense of history that clung to everything like a layer of dust.

"Finish up? What kind of stuff you got cooking?"

"Regular Vampire Slayer stuff. I gotta get Spike."

DENIAL

HE DRAINED THE BLOOD from the stolen plastic bladder into a used coffee cup. A cup of blood and a cigarette for breakfast when the sun goes down. *Doesn't get much better than this*, Spike thought.

Like hell it doesn't. The blood that flowed past his lips tasted cold; it was a frustration he had gotten used to these many, many months he had gone without a fresh kill.

The real frustration was in his heart. Because of *her*.

"So much easier when she wanted to kill me," he said to himself. The thought of her coming to see him almost every night, trusting him, but not allowing herself to get close … he shook it from his mind. The back of his hand wiped the blood from his lips.

He put the empty coffee cup on the top of the TV, threw on his big coat, and left his crypt. The dusk light cast a blue glow over the cemetery. He lit up another cigarette.

Something had happened to Buffy last night, he was sure of it. He hoped it wasn't a big deal.

"Hello, Spike."

"Buffy. Didn't expect to see you so early. I was just thinking—"

She hit him with a right cross to the face.

"Well, look who's all vim and vinegar tonight," he said.

She hit him with a left across the other cheek, this one sending his fresh cigarette tumbling to the ground. It sat there, hissing in the wet grass.

"No more jokes, Spike. You're a vampire. I'm the Vampire Slayer. Add it up."

"I'm not good with the new math, Slayer. But you want a good ol' fashion rough-and-tumble, I'm ready for you."

He put up his fists in a half-mock boxing stance, but she was too fast for him. She littered his face with jabs, and he stumbled under her assault and fell backward. He knew he couldn't fight back, so he had to think of something else.

He managed to pull off a quick backward somersault that put some distance between them, then he took off, heading toward a small crypt on the far end of the cemetery. The thing was built into a low hill and would be perfect for his hastily hatched plan.

Just as he reached the door of the mausoleum, Buffy's hand snapped out and grabbed a fistful of his jacket. He spun quick and sharp, hard enough to throw her balance off. She lost her grip on his coat, and now she was right where he wanted her. He grinned and rubbed the right side of his jaw. That second punch had been one of her best.

"Damn you," she said. "Stand still so I can drive a stake through your heart. I don't have time to fool around and chase you all over the cemetery—I've got a full night. There're vamps to slay, movies to watch …"

He stood there, trying to look relaxed, almost as if he were actually listening to her. He waited for her to close the distance between them. He let her run right into him, spinning just enough so he wouldn't get staked, and used her momentum to toss her right through the entrance of the small crypt. She tumbled down the small flight of steps, and he slammed the door closed.

He'd stumbled across this crypt some time back when checking out the real estate. He'd decided against this particular pad because the latch on the inside was broken. You could get in, you just couldn't get out. He knew it wouldn't hold Buffy for long, but it would keep her shut in long enough for him to get out of there.

"You're out of your head, girl," he shouted through the door. "There's no way you should have fallen for that trick."

He had more to say, but thought it best to go.

† † †

Parnassus Jones slowly opened his eyes. The dream still hung in the air like the sandman's dust floating to the ground. The Goddess of Tears had cradled him in her many arms while she licked the corners of his eyes.

Tell me what you want, she had said.

"I want it all … all the blood, all the props, all the power."

Tell me why you want this.

"It feels so good … so good."

I can make you feel better. Much better. Her sharp teeth had tickled his cheekbone as she spoke.

"What do I have to do? I'll do … anything."

Do you believe that suffering is salvation?

"Yes."

Will you summon the Harvesters?

"Yes."

Then you're almost already there.

Parnassus felt her energy coursing through his body hotter than any drug. He rubbed his hand across the cold metal of the object the Goddess had given him.

Spike didn't know quite what to do. He stopped his anxious stroll though the cemetery and leaned against a tall tombstone, some Egyptian-looking thing. He looked up at it and laughed. The living and their monuments.

He pulled out his dwindling pack of smokes and gave it a little shake. Only a few left. He'd been chain-smoking since he'd locked Buffy in the crypt. He had no idea what that bolt of lightning had unleashed the other night, but something was just not right. He knew what he had to do, but it didn't make him happy.

He slipped a cigarette between his lips and touched it to the butt of his previous smoke. He puffed deeply to get the thing lit. He'd been smoking a long time, and he still loved to hear the sound of the dry tobacco leaves as they started to burn. He tossed the stubby cigarette away and blew out a plume of smoke with a big sigh.

He'd met a few Slayers in his time, and most other Slayers lost their friends and all but abandoned their old life in the endless battle to rid the world of the undead. But not Buffy. Spike had never known any previous Slayer to have such a strong group of friends. He was convinced they made her what she was, and at least part of why he found her so appealing, so irresistible. Even Giles was different, more her friend than her Watcher, a relationship Spike still couldn't figure out. He shook his head and sighed again. Yeah, her friends.

He knew he had to talk to them, get them to help Buffy. But he also knew they didn't like him. He did not look forward to this conversation.

"William, William, William. Fancy meeting you in a cemetery."

Spike whirled, flicking his cigarette out across the cemetery and throwing his fists up, only to see Velatti standing there, arms crossed and a smirk on her face. Spike dropped his guard, upset that he'd tossed away a fresh cigarette.

"Velatti. How long's it been?

"Too long, William."

"Yeah. Funny how vampires lose track of time, isn't it? Might explain some of our kind's ideas about fashion."

They shared a laugh, then an uncomfortable silence fell between them. Spike didn't really know what to say to her. Back when they were hanging out, she'd been so into Parnassus, she never said much to anyone else. But she always had good ideas. That much he did remember.

"So, I was wondering when Parnassus was going to let you out."

"Parnassus doesn't 'let' me do anything. I'm my own woman these days."

Spike stepped back and looked her up and down. He never really looked at her before. Maybe it was because she belonged to Parnassus. Or maybe because back then, he didn't care for anyone other than Dru. Either way, right here, right now, she looked good.

"I will say you're all woman, though."

Before Spike could react, Velatti slammed a quick fist to his nose.

"Ow! Bloody hell!" Spike rubbed his nose. "What was that for?"

"It's a new world, William."

"Yeah, I keep getting that message."

"You look different than I remember." Velatti checked him up and down. "Are you in love?"

"Don't be ridiculous." Spike shoved his hands into the pockets of his coat.

Velatti leaned closer to Spike and looked into his eyes. "You can't hide it. You never had this look when you were with Dru."

"Been great seeing you, Velatti, but I have things to do." Spike, hands still in his pockets, turned and started walking away.

"Wait. I'm heading over to Faint. You should come with."

"No, I don't think so. Not really my scene. Not anymore."

"Come on, it's a big night for Parnassus. You might be interested in seeing his latest plan. You know, like old times."

Spike stopped and his body went rigid. Without turning to look at Velatti, he said, "Old times, huh? What's he got going on?"

"Now, now. That would be telling. But trust me, it's big. Some might say cosmic." Velatti smiled. She knew he'd be there. "We'll be out at the old Hamilton Medical Center, right through the cemetery and down the road."

"When?"

"The ceremony begins at midnight."

"Right, then." Spike laughed to himself. Of course it started at midnight. It always starts at bloody midnight. He strolled off, trying to look cool until he was out of Velatti's sight. Then he broke into a run, heading for Buffy's house.

"Yay! Movie night! Socializing with each other over the pretense of watching a bunch of actors sing and dance their way through emotionally charged but simplistic storylines. It's magical!"

"Ah, Ahn … it's called a *musical*." Xander read the video box as he lounged on the couch in Buffy's living room. After he'd seen Buffy at the shop that morning, he and Anya had a long talk over some hot coffee. Something about his brief conversation with Buffy cleared his mind, and he was able to really open up to Anya, let her know how he felt. Sure, he was still scared about the future, but he figured if he had to be scared, at least he had Anya to be scared with him.

"So, when was Buffy supposed to get here?" Tara poked her head out of the kitchen. She had been keeping quiet, sneaking glances at Willow, who was on the floor, completely enthralled in *The Book of Tears* open on her lap.

"I'm sure she'll be here soon. She said she had a few things to do." Anya fiddled with the VCR. "Oh, darn! Cross-dimensional travel is easier than working this thing. What channel is this supposed to be on?"

"Three, I think," Xander said.

Anya paused a moment. "Buffy did say that she had something to do with Spike. You don't think she's going to invite him, do you?"

"Not likely," Tara said as she walked into the room carrying a monster bowl of popcorn. "Although, I have a feeling Spike would probably enjoy a good musical."

Xander shook his head. "What Spike enjoys he can keep to himself. He may have been somewhat helpful when Buffy was gone, but now—don't need him. Besides, I can't think of anyone who could ruin movie night faster than Spike."

Willow raised her head from the book. "That's amazing."

"Nothing amazing about Spike's ability to ruin—" Xander stopped. "You are talking to *us*, right, Will?"

"Willow, would you *please* put that book away?" Tara squirmed on the couch.

"I will when Buffy gets here. I just can't believe all the powerful stuff in this book. There's this ceremony for summoning the Goddess of Tears. The spells she could give me—big-time powerful."

"At what cost?" Tara said.

Everyone was quiet for an awkward moment.

Xander grabbed a handful of popcorn and put his other arm around Anya. "Ah, hot vid, hot popcorn, hot fiancée, what could be better?"

"Adding hot pizza and a back-to-normal Buffy?" Tara put her chin in the palms of her hands.

"I'll drink to that." Xander held up a bottle of grape Crush.

Anya snuggled against him, and he gave her a loving squeeze. "Now all we need is Buffy. And the pizza."

Willow looked over at Tara. Tara dropped her gaze to the floor. Willow winced, suddenly aware of the silence. Xander and Anya, feeling the awkwardness that filled the room, squirmed on the couch. Xander un-crossed his legs, then re-crossed them.

Tara stood up and walked over to the window. "It's been a weird week. No big bad guys, just routine vampage." She pulled back the curtain over the front window and peered into the darkness. She wished Buffy would hurry.

"Yeah, I haven't cracked a moldy book all week." Xander scratched his head. "And that's a good thing."

"When was the last time we had a week this slow?" Anya looked from Xander to Willow to Tara.

Willow chuckled uncomfortably. "I can't remember, but if I had to guess, I'd say it was right before something really bad happened."

The doorbell rang.

Tara jumped up from her seat. "Ooooh! That must be the pizza. I'll get it."

The door of the small crypt burst open, and Buffy slowly walked out. She knew Spike was long gone. That didn't matter much. She slumped down against a tree, put her head into her hands, and cried.

She was tired of the act she was playing. The wind blew cold on this chilly Southern California night. She looked up to the sky and held onto the Amulet of Arathor. The truth was this: the silence, the loneliness, and the void in her life were all around her stronger than ever.

If she wished hard enough to have her old life back, if she pretended that nothing had changed, then she could be happy.

As she rubbed the amulet, she thought about all of the hardships she had faced over the last several years. It made her feel strong. It gave her the strength to walk back home. She loved her friends so much—it was so hard to be around them since they brought her back. How would they react if they knew? How could she ever tell them?

"Hey, witchy-poo," Spike said as Tara pulled the front door open. He shouldered his way past her and into the living room.

"Spike? What the hell are you doing here?" Xander stood up and pushed the sleeves of his sweater up his forearms.

"We got a problem." Spike shoved his hands into his pockets and stared

hard at Xander. He knew the only reason Xander stood up to him was the chip in his head. When he got his teeth back, though, he'd show him. He'd show them all. But until then, he needed their help.

"Oh, right we do. Of course we do. What were we thinking?" Willow set *The Book of Tears* on the floor and stood up, walking toward Spike but staying just behind Xander. "Oh, wait, you must be confusing *you* with *us* again."

"Yeah, what the hell are you talking about, Spike?" Xander squared his body in front of Spike and balled his fists. "You're not wanted around here."

Spike glowered at Xander. "Don't start something you can't finish. I'm not here to pick a fight, I'm here to talk about Buffy. She's gone off her rocker."

Willow crossed her arms. "No, Spike, you're wrong. Buffy's never been better. She's finally back to normal."

"Normal? She just bloody tried to dust me!"

Xander laughed. "So she's *better* than normal."

"Bollocks! There's no time for this. Some bad business is going down, and we need to get Buffy off my tail and bring her around."

Willow remained indignant. "Spike, we're telling you, there's nothing to bring her around from."

"Look, I hate to burst your blissful bubbles, but that girl is not right in the head. Something happened the other night. That damned lightning did something."

"Lightning?" Xander cocked his head to look at Willow. "Buffy *did* say something about lightning, but I didn't think she meant lightning as in big flash of light in the sky."

Willow threw her hands into the air. "So there was lightning! So what? There's been lightning before, and there'll be lightning again. It doesn't mean that anything is wrong with anybody."

Spike wasn't sure, but he thought he could see the pupil's of Willow's eyes get a little bigger, a little blacker, and he knew. "This lightning was different. And you know it, Red."

"There's only one way to settle this." Willow turned and dropped back into her chair. She looked at Spike, her mouth a hard line. "We'll wait for Buffy. She'll be here any minute. Then we'll settle this."

Spike looked at the clock on the wall. Eleven-thirty.

"Don't have a minute. You see, there's this vamp I used to hang with, a bad number by the name of Parnassus Jones. He's got the whole vampire population in thrall, and tonight, at midnight, he's cutting them loose. Or something. Probably to do with his bloody quest for power. Either way, it's gonna be bad."

"Aw, man. Why's it always gotta be midnight? Where's the creativity with these demon-types?"

Anya answered Xander: "I think the creativity comes in what they actually *do* at midnight."

Spike paused and looked around the room. "Wait … where's the little bit?"

They all stared blankly at him.

"Dawn! Where's Dawn?" Frustrated, Spike waved his arms at their dumb-struck looks. He couldn't believe how dense they could be.

"Oh, Dawnie's at her friend's house. A sleepover," Tara said.

"Sure she is." Spike turned toward the door.

"What's that supposed to mean?" Xander grabbed Spike's shoulder and tried to turn the vampire around.

Spike slapped his hand away, wincing as a small jab of needle-like pain seared his brain, just behind the left eye. Xander took a quick step back, rubbing his wrist. Spike pointed a finger at Xander as he stared down the whole gang.

"I've had it with you people. Too caught up in your own fantasies to see the real truth. And I thought you were supposed to be the good guys."

"We *are* the good guys!" Anya said.

"You're just mad because Buffy finally came to her senses and realized she was better off *without* you." Willow still had her arms crossed.

Spike sighed.

"Whatever, then. I guess this time it's up to old Spike to save the day."

Buffy didn't see the fist coming until it slammed against her nose.

She stumbled backward, losing her footing, and fell flat on her back.

Standing above her was the vamp from the other night, the platinum blonde with the dynamite dress.

"I'd love to kill you, baby. Bag me a Slayer. Mmmm … sounds like fun."

"You're living in a state of denial, lady."

"*Lady?* I might be over a hundred years old, but I'm still younger looking than you. Oh, but I guess I didn't let you know my name the last time we scrapped. I'm Velatti."

The sucker punch had Buffy a little spacey. She shook her head, trying to get her bearings.

"But tonight's your lucky night," Velatti continued. "I've got more important things to do. So instead of a smackdown, we'll have to settle for a little smack."

She grabbed Buffy behind the neck and held her head in place, a perfect target. The Slayer was ready for another cheap shot, but instead of throwing a fist, Velatti leaned in and kissed Buffy hard on the lips. It shocked her even more than the punch to the face.

"We'll do this again sometime. Hitting you is fun." Velatti looked into Buffy's eyes and held her gaze for a moment before taking her hand away and bolting off into the night.

Buffy pulled herself up and wiped her mouth with the back of her hand, then spat on the ground. She ran after the vampire, but when she got to a clearing, she couldn't see anything. Velatti was gone.

Then a bit of laughter made her turn and stop. For a second, she thought maybe she hadn't lost the girl, but as she got closer, she realized the decidedly male-sounding laughter came from three dorky-looking types, talking about the cool party they were heading to. Velatti's types. Vampires.

Buffy stepped out in front of them and smiled as their laughter suddenly stopped.

"Boys, you picked the wrong cemetery to walk into. It's been one bad night, and I'm in the mood to kick some serious ass."

FAINT

"FINALLY! BACK WHERE WE BELONG. I mean, can you believe this place? Faint has got to be the coolest thing to ever hit Sunnydale."

Dawn sighed with a broad smile. "Totally."

Once past the drab, inconspicuous front entrance, she and Melinda took their time strolling down the long corridor. Hanging fluorescent lights lined the ceiling of this old hallway, only the bulbs had been replaced with black lights. The walls were sloppily painted black with splashes of bright color that made the hallway seem to move like an electrified Jackson Pollock painting.

Dawn tried to see what was at the end of this corridor where the music was coming from. But the people who loitered out here, taking a break from dancing, obscured her view. They formed a clot at the hall's end, as if this passage were an artery. As Dawn and Melinda moved forward, the people around them swayed to the invisible flow that wanted to suck them farther inside to the dance floor.

Melinda took out some cigarettes from her purse. "So, you gonna try to hook up with Skeeter?"

"What ... what do you mean?" Dawn declined the cigarette with a hand wave.

"What do you mean, what do I mean? I mean 'hook up' hook up. And since when did you stop smoking?" Melinda lit up.

"It's not like I'm a *smoker*. I smoke when I want to ... I just don't want to right—"

"You don't want people to think we're too young to be here." Melinda forced the cigarette into Dawn's hand. "Come on, I don't want to smoke alone."

Dawn reluctantly took the cigarette. She puffed at it, but choked out the smoke.

They entered the main dance area, which opened up into a large display of decadence. The music seemed to spin around their heads in quadrophonic madness. They had come in from the top floor of what turned out to be an old-fashioned medical-operation theater. Mostly this top floor was like a balcony that overlooked the vast room below. Dawn could see that the walls below had been smashed out, leaving only bare support beams.

They passed the DJ set-up on their way to the stairs opposite the hallway. Melinda nudged Dawn as they descended the steps. "Did you see that big black guy standing behind the DJ? This guy must be one of those famous DJs from L.A. if he has his own bodyguard."

Dawn glanced up at Parnassus and shivered. "If his idea of guarding a body is to scare people, well, mission accomplished."

"Forget that!" Melinda threw out her left hand, hitting Dawn in the chest. "Look!"

"What? What?"

"It's Bobby Malcolm! Heart—be still." Melinda swooned.

"I thought you had a crush on Tyler Williams?"

"Oh, that was *days* ago! Besides, I tried talking to Tyler in the lunch line, and he told his friends I was a butter face."

"Butter face? That's cute," Dawn said.

"No. Guys say that when a girl is good looking … 'but her face.' Screw that. I'm going to go talk to Bobby."

"Don't leave! I don't know anyone here."

"Relax, Summers. This is a rave, so go rave. I'll be right back."

Dawn looked around the room, not sure what to do.

The lights, the people, the music. A girl with huge bug-eye glasses had a fistful of yellow surgical tubing that she was waving around like a whip. Some boy hung upside-down from the edge of the second floor—his hands reaching down into the crowd, and the crowd reaching up and touching his face and chest. Dawn couldn't stop staring at this one couple, making out on an old hospital gurney with an empty IV stand next to it.

Out of this reverie came a voice, then a tap on the shoulder. It startled her.

"Look who showed up! I've been looking for you, Debbie!"

It was Skeeter.

"It's Dawn. Dawn Summers." She noticed he was drinking from one of his own water bottles. The green glow from the light stick flickered in his eyes. "… Are you okay, Skeeter?"

"I'm fine. Dandy, even. Never been better." His body swayed back and forth.

Dawn smiled through the awkwardness in the air. "So, you wanna dance?"

"I'm already dancin', little sistah. Let me ask ya—you've gone all the way, yeah?"

"All the way where?" Dawn immediately blushed. "Oh. Well, it's not like I've never kissed a guy …"

"Awesome. So you're like a total virgin then."

Dawn backed away from him. "What? I can't believe you would say something like that. Are you on drugs or something?"

"Why, you want some?" The way he licked his lips made Dawn's stomach turn.

"I'll see you later, Skeeter—I've got to go find my friend."

He seemed to panic, waving his arms. "No, don't go. I *need* you. I really need you."

"You *what?*"

Parnassus stared out into the crowd, absent-mindedly watching Skeeter slide through the dancers and romancers. Something wasn't quite right with the kid, but it didn't matter as long as he could reel in a virgin. Parnassus laughed. He didn't care what happened to Skeeter after tonight. In fact, he didn't care what happened to anybody.

"Things working out?" A soft voice cooed into his ear.

Parnassus spun, seeing Velatti. She looked flushed, like she just had a good meal or a good fight. Parnassus frowned.

"'Bout time you showed up here, girl. I suppose it's not important to you that I got a big master plan cookin'?"

"Actually, no, it's not important to me. I'm just here for the ride—you'll remember me when you're big and powerful, right?"

"Of course I will, baby. See that yummy little piece?"

"The one talking to Skeeter?"

"Yeah, she's my virgin. I can tell from here."

"Are you sure? Or is the Jube talking to you again?"

"Bitch, I ain't high. Tonight's important—I ain't gonna go messin' 'round with a cheap high when I'm about to blow the roof off of every high I ever had. How come you playin' me?"

"I'm not playing, Parnassus."

"Well, I am. And it's time to get this game going."

"So, let me see if I've got everything straight."

Giles took off his glasses and looked at everyone gathered on the couch. When he'd gotten home after closing up the Magic Box, all four of them were arguing and confused.

"Buffy has been acting normal, which, given the fact that she hasn't acted normal since your spell brought her back from the dead, is actually *not* normal. Spike is acting strangely—which is quite normal—and going on about some vampire named Parnassus who has a take-over-Sunnydale plan happening right now. Buffy is missing. Dawn is at a sleepover. And you all are at odds about what to do next."

Xander nodded his head. "Damn, is this guy good or what?"

"What do you think, Giles?" Tara asked. "Should we wait for Buffy?"

"We have to assume that she's not going to show up soon. It's late, and from what Spike reported, she's on a path of her own." Giles took a deep breath. "Do we know anything else about Parnassus or his ceremony?"

Anya stepped forward. "Let's see, he's probably at some abandoned building—definitely *not* in a good part of town. There's almost certainly a large group of mindless minions. And the ceremony itself—most likely involves the sacrifice of someone innocent."

Xander came up next to her. "Before I shower you with love and affection, can I say … huh?"

"Just a guess. But you know … Vampires. Old habits die hard."

HABITS

"C'MON, DAWN, BABY ... it's no big thing. And I don't know what you're goin' on about. I'm still the same ol' Skeeter everyone knows and loves." He tilted his head back and threw his arms wide. The strobe lights made the wild look on his face even more maniacal.

"No, you're different. Something's really strange." Dawn began looking around nervously for Melinda. When she couldn't see her, she decided to turn and walk away from Skeeter, as far away as she could get.

He grabbed her by the arm and spun her back around, harder than she thought he was capable of.

"Damn, girl, why you illin' all out? Do you know who I am? I'm the king of this action all around you. Faint is my baby. Let me tell you something, Little Miss Fabulous—you wanna get ahead in this world, don't be satisfied with your lot in life. You gotta find something that you want and you gotta want it bad, so bad it becomes a need."

As Dawn struggled against Skeeter's grasp, she became more and more angry. "You're crazy! I can't believe I thought you were cute."

"I'm not crazy—it's just this player knows what it all comes down to. I'm talkin' *sacrifice*. You gotta give to get, you know what I'm sayin'?" Skeeter rubbed his hands together while his eyes got beadier. "I'm gonna give a little something tonight, then I'm gonna get it big. So why don't you come with me and give a little—"

He stopped when he saw Dawn's eyes grow wide as she focused on something over his shoulder. The big black guy Dawn had seen in the DJ booth stood behind Skeeter. He looked happy in a bad, mean way.

"What's up, Shorty? You goin' on at the mouth like a girl," he said. "Don't you have something to do? Somewhere to be?"

"Parnassus. I was—"

"You was leavin' is what you was."

Dawn thought it best to let them argue. She took tiny steps away from them, hoping they wouldn't notice that she was making a break for it. But Parnassus's big hand reached out and grabbed her arm, still sore from where Skeeter had grabbed it.

"My name's Parnassus Jones, little lady. No need to go so soon." He stroked her cheek with the back of his fingers. "My, what nice, pretty, *young* eyes you got."

She watched Skeeter fade back into the crowd. He was giving her a thumbs-up sign that she didn't quite understand. All she knew was she had to get out of here fast.

"You know, I really should check in with my friend." She struggled against his hold.

"You ain't checkin' in on nobody, baby. You checkin' out."

She twisted her arm hard enough to break his grasp. She screamed, backing up into the crowd. Her hands extended out in front of her as she backpedaled through the sea of drugged-up dancers and ravers. No one listened or noticed. Everyone just kept moving to the heavy beat.

"Nowhere to run, girl. You think you'll find help here? Look around you—everybody got their own needs. They ain't gonna be lookin' to you. Let me tell you, the Harvesters are coming. They'll smell your virgin tears, and there's nothin' you can do about it. Nothin'."

Melinda watched as Parnassus moved toward Dawn. She saw the big man holding a strange metal object out in front of him, grasping it with both hands. The tendons on the backs of his hands looked like thick cords and his knuckles flared with white as he struggled with the piece of metal. To Melinda, it looked like he was trying to snap it in two. She wanted to scream and yell and save her friend, but the fear was too much and the situation overwhelmed her.

She ran, leaving Faint and her friend far behind.

Buffy crouched down into a fighting stance. She started a slow, rhythmic breathing, and her eyes flicked across the vamps in front of her as she sized up her foes. Despite everything, she had to hold back a few chuckles. She hadn't fought a group of vamps so out of touch with fashion since her early Slayer days.

The first guy, the one on her left, looked like he hadn't had a bath since his rebirth. A big guy, tough-looking, wearing a pair of baggy army-surplus camo pants. He had a big chain fastened to a belt loop that dangled low and led to a hip pocket, presumably for his wallet. Buffy wondered if he thought it just made him look cool, or if he really carried a wallet.

The second one sported a punker look, almost as dirty as the guy in the camo pants, complete with a dorky soul patch under his bottom lip and backward baseball cap jammed down tight on his head. He looked like a too-chubby version of some guy Buffy had seen on one of Dawn's ever-changing boy-band posters.

The last guy, tall, skinny, and dressed up a little too nice to be hanging out with the other two, wore a seersucker suit and black turtleneck. For some reason, though, he had decided to top off the ensemble with a pair of ski goggles, yellow lenses and all. A mess of hair sprouted from his head, and his long bangs kept falling across his goggles.

Buffy wondered why female vamps seemed to dress so much better than the guys.

"So, who wants to take the first swing at the Slayer?" Chubby adjusted his cap as he looked Buffy up and down.

"Guys, we don't have time for this. Don't ya think we oughtta split ... we gotta get to the—" Goggles looked nervously from side to side, first at

Camo, then at Chubby, trying to talk them out of a fight.

"Zip it, man! You don't want the Slayer finding out about the secret location of the rave and ruining all of our ..." Camo stopped as the words that spilled out of his mouth finally settled in his ears. "Maybe I should shut up now."

"Oh, I don't know. I thought you were doing fine." Buffy rubbed the Amulet of Arathor and felt energy buzz through her body.

Lightning fast, she flipped forward and shot a sharp kick right into Camo's groin. Camo groaned and sunk to his knees, hands over his crotch.

Chubby decided to make his move and charged at Buffy, football-style. Buffy didn't have time to counter-attack, so she side-stepped, grabbing his arm as he torpedoed by and executing a quick judo move that sent Chubby bouncing off the trunk of a nearby tree. This didn't stop him, it just made him angrier. He growled and lowered his head, charging at Buffy like a runaway bull. He was slow—slow enough that she had plenty of time to step aside and pop him in the face with a hard fist.

Chubby's feet slid out from underneath him, and he flopped backward, landing hard in the dirt. He sat there, stunned and blinking. "Wow, man. The lights ... they're awesome ..."

Buffy pulled a stake out of her jacket, spun it once in the palm of her hand and hurled it unerringly into Chubby's heart. He went up in a cloud of dust.

"Next?" Buffy turned back to the remaining two vampires in time to see Camo pull himself to his feet.

"You don't know who you're messing with." Camo rolled his shoulders and stepped forward, all cocky, holding his fists in front of him. "I took karate lessons when I was alive. I'm all like Jet Li ninja action ... and I'm going to bring it down on you something fierce!"

"Hey, dude." Goggles ran a hand through his hair, sliding his bangs out of his eyes. "If you don't cut this out, I'm going to take off ... by myself."

Camo roared and grabbed Goggles by his jacket, just as Buffy kicked at Camo's head. Camo managed to get Goggles in-between his head and Buffy's kick, and the Slayer's foot bounced off Goggles's face, shattering one lens.

"My goggles! Hey, man, not cool! Come on, man, put me down."

"You call that karate?" Buffy took a step back, thinking about her next move. Goggles was the wimp of the bunch, but probably the only smart one. She knew she had to keep him alive, at least long enough to get any information.

Camo swung Goggles back around, using him as a weapon, and slammed him chest first into Buffy's face. The skinny vampire, hanging like wet laundry in Camo's grip, grunted and sputtered as Buffy rapid-punched Goggles in the chest.

Buffy stepped back and pulled out a stake. She stabbed at Goggles. Camo, anticipating her move, let go of Goggles and jumped backward out of the way. But at the last second, Buffy spun around, kicking Goggles along the side of the head. A sharp crack rang though the night. Goggles flew through the air, landing in a sprawling heap at the foot of a nearby gravestone.

Camo looked up at Buffy. She smiled and threw the stake.

"And besides, Jet Li doesn't 'do' karate. He's a master of wushu. Get it right!"

Before Camo had time to realize he should run, he felt the stake pierce his chest, and he exploded into dust. Buffy slapped her arms, trying to get the vampire dust out of her clothes. She began walking over to where Goggles had fallen, but he wasn't there. She looked up and saw him running out of the cemetery, heading for a narrow alley. Why did they have to run? She took off after him.

Goggles looked back over his shoulder and didn't see the feisty blonde girl running after him anymore. He must have lost her in the maze of alleyways next to the cemetery. He slowed down to a jog. He felt like his lungs were about to explode. He knew it was a ludicrous concept; he didn't have to breathe. But his mind was telling him that his lungs hurt. Not enough fresh blood lately or something. He stopped moving altogether and leaned against the brick wall of a building bordering the alley.

The punch came out of nowhere and almost knocked his jaw off. Goggles fell to the ground, writhing in pain, holding onto the side of his face that had impacted with Buffy's fist.

"Oh, no. Please, no." Goggles began a backward, crab-like scramble away from Buffy.

Buffy bent down and grabbed Goggles by the front of his jacket, jerked him to his feet, and slammed him against the brick wall. She pulled the broken ski goggles over his head and threw them down the alley, then glared into his eyes.

"Now, how about telling me all about this 'secret' location."

Dawn screamed.

Parnassus kept moving forward, and Dawn kept backing up, until they reached the center of the dance floor. Still, no one noticed, made any attempt to help, or even react.

Dawn couldn't move. She wanted to, desperately. Her mind was screaming, Go!, but her body wouldn't listen; she felt numb and distant from herself, almost like this was happening to a different Dawn Summers. Even though she knew Parnassus was coming after her, she was troubled by the fact that he was concentrating on the chalice he held in his hands.

It glowed from the reflections of the many lights. Parnassus held it in a way that made her think it was holding him. He began to shake.

Dawn held her breath.

Still shaking, face contorted with effort, Parnassus snapped the object in two. He set the pieces by her feet, one on either side of her. She couldn't move, and she had to remind herself to breathe again. And that's when the *really* bad things started to happen.

First, she noticed the noise. As she struggled to take a breath, she could hear it cut through the music, a high frequency sound, like an alarm, that cut right to the base of her skull.

Then she noticed a strange kind of movement in the periphery of her vision, like the edges of the room starting to melt. She thought the lights were getting dimmer, but she realized it was something in the building; a dark wave rolling closer to her.

The lights started to pierce through this darkness.

It glittered with prism-like colors, like the wave was filled with gems.

But they weren't gems. They were wings.
"Damn, she said they'd be magnificent, but just look at them beauties." Parnassus had fallen to his knees.
"The Harvesters of Tears are in the house!"
Dawn fought to swat them

away, but the more she waved her hands, the harder it became to move. She felt them land on her arms, then she began to

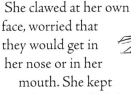

feel them on her face.
She clawed at her own face, worried that they would get in her nose or in her mouth. She kept coughing, terrified that she would breathe them in.
Dawn began to cry.

The room seemed to fall silent as the Harvesters crawled up her face. She could feel them in this frozen moment, little insect tongues licking the corners of her eyes. Drinking her tears.

Parnassus twitched in his ecstatic state. He held his hands palm up, waiting, waiting He watched on as Dawn's tears fell upwards and formed a cloud above her head.

Soon the cloud began to take on shape. It looked like an opening.

"She's coming," Parnassus muttered through wet lips. "Baby, she's coming."

Parnassus Jones began to cry. It was the most beautiful thing he'd ever seen.

Buffy stared at the weather-worn sign that read *Hamilton Medical Center*. Right next to it, hanging on a rusting chain-link fence, a *No Trespassing* sign stared back at her. She sighed. According to Goggles, this was supposed to be the place where the big party was going down. Even as Goggles spluttered and choked out the details between whimpers, Buffy thought an old hospital seemed like an odd place for a party. And now that she was here, she had even more doubt. There weren't even any lights.

She looked around. No vamps in sight. She sighed again. It seemed too quiet for a party anyway.

She froze when she heard a twig snap, not too far away. As quietly as she could, she scurried behind a tree. She got hidden just as two vamps came running into the clearing and stopped in front of the sign.

"Man, I hate that this party keeps moving around."

"Don't be an idiot, man. It's gotta change or it's gonna get busted. 'Sides, we're here now. Let's go get some."

"Yeah, I hope there are more goodies here tonight."

"You bet they'll be here … just don't you go and bogart my chew again, bro. This time, you find your own."

Buffy watched the pair squeeze through a split in the fence and walk toward the broken-down medical center. She thought about rushing after them, turning them to so much dust, but she stopped herself. She grabbed the amulet around her neck and felt a serene calm flood her body. There was a time for raw vengeance, and there was a time for stealth. Thanks to the Amulet of Arathor, she was able to tell the difference.

She walked up to the fence, trying to stay in the shadows, and watched as the two vamps looked left, then right, then scurried through a boarded-up window next to the main entrance of the medical center. "I don't know what I'd do without this amulet."

"I imagine you'd kick ass like you always do."

Buffy whirled around, throwing up her fists. She rolled her eyes when she saw who was standing there behind her.

"Spike! You got nothing better to do than sneak up on people?"

"I got plenty better to do, like wonder why you've been going all funny farm. And now I know. It's 'cause of that gaudy necklace you been wearing lately."

"This is no ordinary gaudy necklace. This is the Amulet of Arathor."

"Amulet of Arathor? Never heard of it."

"That's not *my* problem." Buffy pointed across the wide, empty parking lot toward the squat shadow of the medical center. "What's going on inside here, *that* is."

"Yeah, the nasties are loose inside." Spike pointed at the Amulet of Arathor. "But you've got your own bit of nastiness right there. You're letting it make decisions for you. You're not thinking clearly. You don't need it."

"I tell you what I don't need—*your* advice."

"You bloody well need someone's advice, and I've been around long enough to know when to steer clear of things with a bad influence."

Buffy laughed. "Give me a break. You're a walking, talking bad influence, and *I've* been around long enough to know to steer clear of *you*."

"But you can't, can you? Sooner or later you'll realize that you and I are not so bad—"

"Don't!" Buffy jabbed a finger up at Spike's face. "You are *wrong*. The two of us will never be anything but bad. I can tell what you're thinking and … just don't!"

"Right, then." Spike smirked and jerked his chin at the dilapidated building. "In the meantime, you're gonna need someone to watch your back inside there if you're going up against Parnassus Jones, Velatti, and a whole horde of bloodsucking types. And who better than old Spike?"

Buffy looked from Spike to the medical center, then back to Spike. Subconsciously, her hand settled on the amulet about her neck. She rubbed the gem, then blew out a puff of air in a big sigh.

"Fine. But we stick to business. No more about … you know."

"Business it is. Plenty of heads in there that need knocking." Spike swept an arm out toward the tear in the fence. "After you."

Buffy glared hard at Spike, then turned and slipped through the fence. Spike followed closely behind her, smiling as she squirmed through the gap in the chain links.

Dawn's tears had been used up. The Harvesters were gone. But Parnassus, his tears flowed fast and free.

He was still focusing on the cloud portal above Dawn's unconscious body. The portal glowed bright gold, and from its opening came multiple arms. They reached like tentacles toward Parnassus.

"O my Goddess, bring it on. I've done what you've asked."

Finally the crowd started to take some notice. But most everyone was so drugged out that they thought this was part of the entertainment at Faint. Some kids applauded; others ignored it and made out in the corners. The music played on.

Parnassus couldn't believe this was really about to happen. He could taste the feeling starting to come on, as his mind raced through thoughts of his favorite highs. His mind was clean, and he knew it was the perfect state to take all that the Goddess had to offer.

But something was wrong. He stopped moving. His eyes narrowed. And with his mouth wrinkled in a scowl, his face morphed into vampire mode.

He spun around to see Skeeter holding a stake down at his side. He reached out and grabbed the kid by the puffy fabric of his vest.

"Boy, you wanna be a vampire, first thing you gotta learn is sharp pieces of wood like that, they's dangerous."

Skeeter dropped the stake.

"D-d-dude, this is so not what it looks like … okay, I know that s-sounds retarded—"

Parnassus held him a couple inches off the ground. "Retarded? Shorty, you playin' the wrong game. I was bustin' out love on you left and right. Now you gots to do me like this. You got no love for the Parnassus—he got no love for you."

He jerked Skeeter around and grabbed him by the neck, putting his lips next to the kid's ear. "I was gonna take you to the next level. That's what we talked about. But you blew it, Shorty, ya blew it all up. You know how?"

"I'm sorry, man. Really, please don't—"

Parnassus smacked him upside the head. "You forgot about the fishes."

"F-f-fishes?"

"That's right. Fishes. See there's little fishes and there's big fishes and look around you—what you see here is a big damn pond."

His thumbnail cut into Skeeter's neck as he continued. "You may want things, you might got yourself some needs, but realize you're swimmin' in the big pond now."

"No, wait, man. I know how it is, and I know it ain't like that. I've been paying attention, and it's—"

The taste of blood filled Parnassus's mouth, and the Jube in Skeeter's system put a hard buzz on him. Everything turned a warm, electric red.

"Okay, time to spring into action! Get out the research books! Figure out where this Parnassus guy is holding this ceremony! Put the kibosh on it!" Willow looked at Xander and crossed her arms. "Nothing we haven't done before, right?"

"Uh, do you guys have any idea how many abandoned buildings there are in Sunnydale?" Xander turned around the room to make sure everybody heard him. "There's gotta be more abandoned buildings than there are graves!"

"Really, Xander. I'm sure there is a surplus of abandoned buildings in town, but there's no need to resort to hyperbole."

"Well, hyperbole or not, we need to quickly figure out which one of the

buildings Parnassus is using," Tara said, taking Willow's hand. The two girls looked at one another and smiled, as if in the shadow of crisis, all wrongs were forgotten—until Willow looked down at *The Book of Tears*, lying on the floor. Tara caught her glance and let Willow's hand drop from hers as the frustration and jealousy she'd been feeling the past few days raged through her again.

"Well, that's the trouble." Giles sighed, removing his glasses. "We're very good at figuring out how to defeat demons, but, with the possible exception of Xander, I doubt any of us have the remotest idea of where to start looking up vacant buildings."

"You mean besides the Internet." Willow started for the steps. "Let me get my PowerBook."

"Ah, yeah. Good idea, but do we have the time to search every vacant building in Sunnydale in—" Xander looked up at the clock. "—Fifteen minutes?"

"There's no way we can figure this out in time." Giles shoved an errant pillow aside and sat down on the couch. "Blast."

"We can't be stumped." Anya sat forward and let her head drop into her hands. "I don't like this being stumped. When this has happened before, the answer was right there in front of us all the time. It's got to be like that this time, right?"

A loud pounding echoed through the house, and everyone slowly turned to look at the front door.

"That's gotta be Spike, coming back for Buffy." Xander slammed a fist into the palm of his hand. "I can't believe I'm saying this, but I'm glad. He'll know where this place is."

Xander stormed over to the front door and pulled it open. Then he immediately jumped back when a girl fell into the house and collapsed across the threshold.

"Oh, thank God you're here!" The girl looked up at them with red-rimmed eyes and began to cry.

"Who the devil is that?" Giles jumped up from the couch, pointing at the girl with his glasses.

"Melinda? What are you doing here?" Willow rushed over and crouched down next to Melinda and began to gently help her up. "I thought you were with Dawn."

"I ... I was. But ... Dawn's in trouble!"

"Trouble? But ... she was at your house," Tara said, slipping an arm around Melinda's back, helping Willow get Melinda into the living room.

The girl shivered and sobbed as they got her settled onto the couch. Tara put a blanket over her, and Melinda looked up, trying for a smile but grimacing instead. She had just gotten her crying under control, but now her bottom lip started to quiver, and she burst into tears all over again.

Tara leaned close, stroking Melinda's hair to calm her down. "It's okay now. Tell us about it."

Melinda, comforted by the safety of Tara's touch, sniffled and started to talk. "We went to this party, in an old hospital, and this scary guy grabbed Dawn, and he had this thing, and, oh, God! I had to run. I'm sorry."

"It's okay." Tara pulled Melinda up into a hug, patting her on the back.

Melinda screamed, shattering the fragile sense of serenity that had briefly settled over the room. Everyone jumped and looked at Melinda, who sat on the couch, screaming and pointing. Everyone's eyes followed to *The Book of Tears*, still lying closed on the floor.

"The ... the guy, the one w-who ... took Dawn ... he had ... *that thing!*"

Willow picked the book off the floor and held it up. "Wait ... this? The book?"

Melinda shook her head, then dropped her face into her hands.

"This symbol?" Willow tapped the embossed icon on the cover of *The Book of Tears*.

Melinda looked up for a second and nodded before letting herself collapse back onto the couch, a spasm of tears wracking her body. Tara rubbed her back, whispering to her that everything was going to be okay.

"Oh, boy, this is not good." Willow looked up at Xander. "We need to get to this place, and fast. Dawn is in serious trouble."

"Okay, okay. Let me think. Old hospital ..." Xander started pacing, then snapped his fingers. "That's gotta be the Hamilton Medical Center; it's just gotta be. They're tearing it down next month. If Dawn's in trouble we have to go now."

"Right." Giles slipped his glasses on. "Let's gather some weapons and get going."

"I'm bringing this." Willow tucked *The Book of Tears* under her arm. "We might need it."

Tara looked at Giles, but he'd already left the room. She frowned and smoothed the blanket over Melinda, trying to hold back her own tears.

Dawn woke up next to Skeeter's dead body. But that wasn't the worst thing.

Above her was a cup of gold light, and from this light the Goddess of Tears reached out for Parnassus. Even though Dawn felt like she could move again, all of her muscles didn't agree with her. She stayed frozen to that spot.

Most of the crowd stood there with their heads craned back, gazing in awe of the spectacular vision of something so powerful crossing dimensions.

Parnassus kept blinking, trying to stay focused himself. The Jube was creeping deeper into his pleasure center. He wanted more—he had to have it now before the come-back-down vibe started shaking him loose.

"Finally. The goods have been delivered, now bring on the flavor."

Parnassus, the tears were only the first taste to get me here.

"First ... taste?"

Yes. I'm in a very fragile state ... I need more.

"I don't got no more. You're supposed to give me the more."

Silly, simple vampire. Mine are not the hands from above to lift you up. I feed on the suffering of the worlds below me. Look at your sad world. So filled with the suffering of innocents ... you've fed upon them too. But it's not enough. I must have more.

Parnassus gritted his teeth to try to settle the effects of the Jube. He wasn't sure he understood what she was telling him.

"No more talkin' ... you gotta hook me up. I just need enough to take me ..."

Her arms surrounded him. She placed a hand on his chest.

I'll take your suffering away. Then I'll come and take the suffering away from the rest of the world.

Her fingers pierced his rib cage. Light filled the room.

No matter how much you want, no matter how much you need, it will always be the same for us, Parnassus. You and I are creatures of habit. And it is never enough.

Dawn could see what was coming. She had no more tears and very few screams left. She put her hands over her eyes, curled up in a ball, and hoped that no one would notice her. But she couldn't help peeking through her fingers. And when she did, she saw a platinum blonde with a wooden stake yell at the Goddess.

"Sorry, bitch, but killing him is my business!" Velatti stood confident behind Parnassus.

She thrust the stake into his back.

Light flowed from his eyes as he began to turn to dust. The Goddess of Tears made a sound of total anguish.

Then everything went dark.

SERENITY, COURAGE, WISDOM

As soon as Buffy and Spike started down the dark corridor, they could hear the heavy bass thumping through the building. Buffy assumed some magic kept her from hearing the music outside the building. Or maybe it was the strange acoustics of the place. Either way, it didn't matter. She was going to shut it down.

Up ahead of them at the end of the corridor Buffy and Spike could see flashing colored lights. They walked cautiously, creeping past the undulating couples groping in the dark and the incoherent, drug-addled kids collapsed along the wall.

"What are these people up to? Is this supposed to be entertainment?"

"Well, yeah." Spike jumped, avoiding a pair of legs that suddenly sprung out from some twitching kid lying along the wall. "If I was younger, this is where I'd be. Prime feeding ground, this."

"Spike, you disgust me."

"That tune is getting a little stale, Slayer. Might want to sing a new one."

"I'll change mine when you change yours."

"I have changed, and you know it. You just refuse to admit it."

Buffy grabbed the sleeve of Spike's arm, spinning him around. She looked up into his face with a hard, cold, stare. "I thought we agreed to leave this outside."

"You started it." Spike pulled his arm away from Buffy.

Buffy paused, still staring hard at Spike. "And now I'm finishing it."

"Fine, then. Let's clean house." Spike stormed off ahead, forgetting caution and stealth.

Buffy waited a moment, watching Spike's silhouette as he walked into the flashing lights of the room beyond the corridor. She felt the cool metal of the amulet against her neck, then followed behind Spike.

Spike came out of the corridor into a round room with a high domed ceiling and found himself standing on a balcony that ran around the whole room and overlooked the floor below. He looked down just in time to see the large, ghostly shape reach its hands right into his old friend Parnassus Jones. Even considering all Spike had been through in his time, this was a strange scene.

Buffy ran up beside Spike just as a bright light exploded into the room, blinding both of them for a second. They shaded their eyes, unable to look away. Then, as quickly as it appeared, the light vanished.

As Spike blinked, trying to get the bright spots out of his eyes, he saw the green dust that used to be Parnassus fall to the ground, and Velatti standing there holding a long, sharp stake. Velatti looked up at Spike and grinned.

All Buffy saw was her sister, curled into a small ball, surrounded by a mad, sweaty mob, and lying on the floor next to a dead body and a certain evil platinum-blonde vampire.

"Dawn? Oh, God. Dawn!" Before she even realized it herself, Buffy hurled herself over the railing.

"Buffy, wait! We need to—" Spike flung out an arm, grabbing for Buffy, fingers just brushing her as she fell to the floor below.

"Ah, what the hell." Spike took a step back, got a running start, and jumped over the railing after Buffy.

When Buffy and Spike hit the floor the DJ scratched the record to a stop. Everyone stopped dancing. Without the music, Buffy could practically hear the eyes turn toward her and the faces change to their vampire form.

Easily half the crowd were vampires. The other half was a bunch of dazed and confused kids who finally realized that all this wasn't part of the show. Silence hung in the air for a few tense heartbeats, then the room exploded with screams and flailing limbs as the humans began to flee.

The vampires formed a crowd around Velatti. She faded back into this mass of friends. With a tiny wave, she bid farewell to Buffy.

"Spike, make sure Dawn is safe—I'm going after Velatti," Buffy said.

Spike nodded and bolted through the crowd. Getting Dawn wouldn't be easy. Spike saw her scramble through the chaos of vamps on the attack and non-vamps struggling to get away.

The place was packed so tightly,
the arms that grabbed at her were like stinging
brambles.

Dawn had
no idea where she was
running to. She just knew
that she had to keep moving.
Every time someone grabbed her arm, she twisted and turned and darted off in another direction. She could hear Spike calling after her. She would have loved to run to him—she knew he wouldn't let anything happen to her. But she couldn't find his voice, and she knew she couldn't stay still.

She was crawling through the forest of legs, trying to avoid being stomped. As she pushed past someone's leather-covered thigh, a face poked out at her.

"Boo, little girl. Come dance with me."

She pushed at the vamp's face, feeling his wrinkled forehead. It sent chills up her arm and down her back. She scrambled along the floor, but the vamp crawled right after her.

"Come on, sweet thing. One little dance. It won't mean a thing. You don't even have to kiss me."

"Buffy! Spike! Somebody help me! I'm down here!"

She thought she heard someone call back, but the voice seemed so far, far away.

Then someone grabbed her shoulders. She could feel a hot, foul breath on her neck.

She kicked and scratched at the vamp who grabbed her. The leering face of the vamp who had been chasing her along the floor loomed close. He smiled. But the smile didn't last. Dawn saw a hand reach out from behind the vamp and tap him on the shoulder.

"Look, pal, the lady doesn't want to dance with you. Besides, she's with me."

Dawn's heart jumped when she realized she knew that voice. Xander.

It was her turn to smile when she saw Xander punch the vamp in the face. The vamp let go of her shoulders and stumbled backwards, only to explode when Xander shoved a stake through the surprised monster.

"Xander! How …" Dawn was shaking with relief.

"We'll fill you in on the Melinda of it all later. Now, we got to shake our booties out of here."

As she got to her feet she saw Willow, Tara, and Anya behind Xander. They all held stakes, points out at the ready. All except Willow—she had a large leather-bound book in her hands. When Dawn ran forward and hugged Xander, she saw Giles not too far away, shooting crossbow bolts into some of the vampires who had been chasing her. She smiled and couldn't help thinking that he didn't look so old when he was holding a crossbow.

"Why aren't you with Dawn?"

Spike's back was to Buffy. All the other vamps had formed a wide circle around them.

"Looks like the Good Humor gang beat me to it. Just as well, I figure. That leaves me free to help you in the Slay-athlon."

Buffy whipped out a pair of stakes, one in each hand, and thrust them forward just in time to dust the two lead vampires in the throng rushing her.

Spike whipped his coat aside and pulled out an axe, then, in a single motion, beheaded three vampires as the mob tightened around them.

"An axe? Where did you pull that out of?" Buffy round-kicked and stabbed, dusting the vamps as fast as they could come.

"Wouldn't you like to know?" Spike adjusted his grip on the axe, and, before he could swing it again, got overwhelmed by another vampire.

"You're impossible! Why do you insist on following me around?" Buffy ducked as a wiry vamp swung a fist at her head. She thrust a stake up into his chest.

"You know. It's because …" Spike thrust his axe forward, pushing the big vamp back into the mass of attackers.

"Don't you *dare* say it." Buffy moved fast, swinging and thrusting wildly, sending up clouds of vamp dust in her wake.

"You can't deny the truth. At least not forever." Spike tugged on his axe, but the point seemed to be stuck in the vamp's chest. He kicked up at the vamp, slamming a boot into its face.

"What truth? Do you even hear yourself? You're a vampire, Spike. I'm the Slayer." Buffy took a hard punch to the face, then another to the chest. She rolled with the blows, spinning backward, and slammed a stake into a vamp.

"A perfect match made in hell." Spike swung the axe in an overhead arc, cleaving a big vamp's skull.

"Spike. I do *not* need you around. Will you get that through your head?"

Buffy saw two vamps coming at her, one from each side. She jabbed her arms out, impaling them both.

"You're lying to me and to yourself. Admit it." Spike followed through with his swing and took the heads off two more vamps.

"No!" Buffy spun around, a stake in each hand, thrusting them right at Spike's chest.

Spike moved quickly, dropping his axe to catch Buffy's hands. He held her arms wide, and they stood there, breathing hard, staring into each other's eyes, faces inches apart.

"I think we're done here."

Spike leaned in to Buffy, moving his mouth closer …

Buffy jerked her hands away from Spike and looked around the room. She kept her guard up. The room, now covered in green dust, was empty except for her and Spike. And the boy's body at her feet. She slipped her stakes into her back pocket and looked down at the body, wondering who this kid was.

Spike reached into his coat and pulled out a pack of cigarettes, then put one in his mouth.

"You're always looking for excuses for why it can't work between us. I don't buy it. Sooner or later, they'll disappear." Spike lit the cigarette dangling from his lips, then pointed at Buffy's neck. "Like your precious necklace."

Buffy reached for her throat. The Amulet of Arathor was gone.

"Spike, what kind of trick—"

"No trick. I just noticed it myself. Must have fallen off—"

A light crunching sound came from behind her. She turned to see her friends had walked into the room. She breathed a sigh of relief when she saw Dawn, a little scuffed up but otherwise safe. Then she noticed that Xander stood there holding his left foot in the air. Her breath froze in her chest.

"Oops. That can't be good. Unless good is found in thousands of little pieces." Xander shrugged at her.

Buffy's face went vacant. "My … my energy amulet. It's … it's gone."

Anya scrunched up her face. "Energy amulet? What energy amulet?"

"Huh? The one you gave me, you know, the Amulet of Arathor."

"No, no, you've got it all wrong. The Amulet of Arathor doesn't have any magical properties. At least none that I know of."

"It doesn't?"

"No. I got a whole shipment of them off of QVC." Anya glanced around at the group's blank stares. "I just thought it would cheer her up. And it looked good with her skin tone."

"It *did* look good on you, Buffy." Tara shrugged.

"Anya, am I to understand that you're buying cheap baubles from a crass commercialized television program to sell in my store?"

"*Our* store. But they *do* sell, Giles. It's a magic shop, and we should diversify a little." Anya held a hand up in front of Giles and rubbed her thumb across her fingers, the universal sign for money. "You know, keep the cash flow moving with new product lines?"

"No matter. What's important, here, is that Buffy realized …" Giles sighed. No one was listening to him, something he'd gotten used to recently. These kids didn't need him anymore. He would miss them, yes, but he wanted to go home.

"Hate to say I told you, Slayer, but I told you." Spike sucked in a long drag of cigarette smoke.

Dawn waved a hand in front of her face. "Spike, you smoke too much."

Buffy bent down and picked up the axe Spike had dropped. She tested its weight and gave it a mock swing. It whistled sweetly through the air. She looked at her sister and friends. Did she still belong here, with this group of people? No matter how much she tried to ignore it or cover up her feelings, they still felt so different to her. The silence began to close in around her. An uncomfortable wave washed over the group. They all stared at Buffy, then as if everyone had the same thought, all eyes turned away. An awkward silence filled the air.

"Well, we win again!" Willow threw a victory fist in the air.

Buffy looked at her and forced a smile. Then she saw what was in Willow's hands. Anger and resentment flooded her as she remembered the peace she felt. The peace she'd been torn from.

"Willow, why did you bring that book?"

"Oh, now that's a long story. Let's go over these details at home. We still have time to salvage movie night. And with everything that's happened, let's just be glad that big bad vamp never got to start the ceremony. Because, oh boy, according to this book, if the ceremony would have been interrupted and the Goddess of Tears had been trapped in *this* dimension …"

A low rumbling rolled through the room.

"Ah, Willow?" Buffy grasped her axe with both hands. "I don't think this night's over yet."

TEARS

THE GODDESS OF TEARS stepped out from the dark corner of the room, hunched over, and began scuttling across the floor. Her arms had shriveled up into long, bony spindles. The skittering sound they made against the ground sounded worse than the high-pitched shrill that came from her mouth.

Spike laughed. "So this is our Cracker Jack prize for fighting through a box of raved-up vamps? A big bug? Well, bring 'er on."

He ran at her with all of his macho bravado. He made her out for a large, easy target. Start grabbing her legs and snap them like kindling. They'd be on their way home in no time.

But when he stopped running, she was gone.

"Nice move, Spike," Xander yelled. "Chase the monster back into the shadows where we *can't* see it."

Spike turned and gave Xander a two-finger gesture. "If I wanted fighting advice from you—"

The Goddess's hairy claws shot out at Spike and lifted him high in the air. She spun him around in her nimble hands like a spider playing with a caught fly.

She tired of her toy and tossed him aside. He hit one of the many exposed support beams, and he crumpled, unconscious, to the ground. She turned her head toward the rest of the group, looking for her next toy.

Buffy spun her axe in her hands. "Xander, you and Anya make sure Dawn is safe—try to get her out of here."

Anya put her arm around Dawn. "Don't worry, Xander will find a way to get us out. He's much smarter than Spike. And much cuter."

"Thanks, Ahn. Now that we have the rousing encouragement taken care of, all we need is a distraction. Any suggestions, Giles?"

The monster lowered her head to the ground and came at Giles. Buffy stepped in front of the attack path. The Goddess stopped, reared her head back, and screamed.

Giles wiped the sweat from his forehead and slipped another quarrel into his crossbow, knowing that it really wouldn't do any good. "Willow, I certainly hope that enormous book of yours has an answer or two for our current predicament."

Willow cradled the book in her left arm as she frantically flipped through the pages. "There are any number of spells I could try … I'm just not sure that I have what it takes. If I could get a little magic boost, just to get me through these incantations …"

She held her right hand in the air toward the towering Goddess of Tears. "No glot c'lom fliday!"

A blue flare lit up the dark building. Its light soaked into the skin of the Goddess and did more to energize the monster than to stop her.

Tara cried out: "I th-think it w-wants the spells. Like it's feeding off your p-power, Will."

Willow had fallen to her knees. She didn't say anything back to Tara. Instead, she kept flipping through the pages, looking for that elusive spell. Something just a little bigger, just a little better.

Giles raced over to the girls. He leaned down to comfort Willow. When he looked up at the Goddess, he saw one of her claws swing toward his face. It caught his cheek, and he sailed across the floor, crossbow flying from his grip.

Buffy felt the weapon in her hand and was ready to do things her way. She checked the other side of the room one more time to see Xander, Anya, and Dawn trying to make it up the stairs. She jumped into action, swinging the battleaxe with all her strength.

She was already in the midst of her second swing when she realized that the axe had gone straight through the monster's body with no apparent damage whatsoever.

"Come on, Willow … I could really use your help here, please. We're a little light on the damage department."

"I'm trying, Buffy. I can't believe this book is so filled with … such lies. There has to be something I'm missing … something that is right under my nose."

A short burst of laughter echoed from above. Buffy knew immediately who it was.

Velatti stood at the top of the stairs with her hands on her hips. She had just managed to jump out from her hiding place and block Xander, Anya, and Dawn's escape route. Dawn looked over her shoulder; the Goddess was headed right for them.

"I was going to escape, disappear, get the hell outta this silly town. The only reason I came to Sunnydale was to get revenge on Parnassus, humiliate him publicaly, to show him that throwing me away was a mistake." Velatti stared the Goddess of Tears right in the face. "This great big cosmic badness was the whipped cream on top of my pie. Then I realized that you, Slayer, you were too tempting to leave behind."

Xander and Anya shared a knowing glance. They each grabbed one of Dawn's hands and ran down the stairs, directly toward the Goddess, easily running between the towering monster's legs. They joined up with Willow, Tara, and Giles. The witches were holding hands, and suddenly a magical protection bubble surrounded them all.

The Goddess leaped into the air, her agility belying her size. She landed on the force field, and her legs made a sizzling sound as the magic seared them.

She skittered off into the darkness of the bottom floor.

Buffy tossed her axe to the ground and pulled out a wooden stake. She stepped in between Velatti and her friends.

"You got a lucky, blind punch in last time," Buffy said. "Your luck now? Just ran out."

Buffy and Velatti went at each other. They both stood strong, handing out punches and taking some more in return.

"No wonder Parnassus dumped you—you're all style and no substance. Oh, and really … not all *that* much style."

"Honey, you only wish you had my style. Maybe I'll turn you. I'm sure if we had eternity, I could teach you *something*."

Velatti took a tough combination of jabs to the face, stepped back, and shook them off.

"No, on second thought," she rubbed her jaw, "I'd rather kill you."

Buffy spun around and planted a reverse kick across Velatti's temple.

Velatti staggered back into the edge of the shadows.

"Kill me? You'd be lucky to even challenge me."

Velatti smiled. "I'll do better than that. I'll—"

A sound cut her off. A sound, a flash of light, a blur of motion. The Goddess of Tears pounced on top of Velatti. The monster sunk her knife-like teeth into the vampire's shoulder.

"That's it!" Dawn yelled. "I know how to send this big freako back to whatever hell place she calls home!"

Dawn broke through the protection bubble and ran toward the Goddess.

Buffy cried out: "Dawn! No!"

The Goddess had Velatti's limp body in her multiple arms. She tossed her around the same way she had played with Spike earlier.

Dawn reached down near the Goddess's feet and grabbed what she was looking for off the ground: the two halves of the object Parnassus had broken.

Velatti let out a whoosh of air as the Goddess threw her across the room. Her body hit another wooden support beam and snapped it into splinters.

Dawn rushed back to safety of the magic bubble; Willow and Tara let her in.

Giles asked, "What is that? A smashed artifact of some sort?"

"Dawnie, you're brilliant!" Willow leaned over to kiss Dawn's forehead.

The room began to shake. The Goddess held her head high and pushed her many arms up to the ceiling. Debris rained down from above, and soon part of the second floor, weakened by the broken support beams, crashed down, crushing Velatti's body under tons of plaster and cement.

Buffy picked her axe up from the ground. "One little girl down, one big girl to go. Willow, what's the good news?"

"Dawn found the device that started the ceremony, right, Dawn?"

Dawn nodded her head. She took the two pieces in her hands and placed them together. Blue light poured forth from the device, now complete again.

"You're right, Willow." Giles stood up and smiled. "Look at the way it's affecting the beast."

The Goddess scurried in circles, moving frantic and nervous, like a dog hearing a high-pitched sound.

Then she stopped. She stood still, standing at full height. Her jaws were the only thing that moved as she tried to form the words.

I can … take your suffering … away … I … I just need … a little more …

Buffy swung her axe and felt a solid thud as it connected with a wet sound. She paused.

"They say you're a Goddess. That makes me think that you're supposed to be better than me."

Buffy's axe hit again, making solid contact to the creature's pale flesh.

"But when I look at you, all I see is a big hole—a giant void that can't be filled."

Buffy swung the axe again and again. The sharp blade sloshed through pulpy flesh each time until, finally, the Goddess fell to the floor. She lay there, her torn and battered body twitching slightly, looking as if she'd been reduced to nothing but a deflated balloon.

"You say you have needs? Well, I have needs too." Buffy raised the axe over her head in both hands and brought it down hard into the mass of quivering flesh.

The final blow sunk deep into the creature's body. A second later she was gone, her body exploding into a blue cloud, the way a staked vampire explodes into dust.

But this wasn't dust. The spray from the explosion covered everyone with mist.

"Yuck!" Xander wiped the clear liquid from his face.

Dawn wiped her mouth with her sleeve. She spit on the ground. "Ew. It tastes funny. It's salty … like seawater."

Buffy dropped her weapon.

"Not seawater, Dawn. It's tears."

An awkward moment hung in the air with no one really knowing what to say. Giles put his hand on Willow's shoulder.

"I guess you didn't need that book after all."

"Of course I don't *need* it." Willow threw the large book onto a pile of debris. She pointed to where it landed and said confidently, "*Aufwaermen!*"

The Book of Tears went up in flames.

"See? Bad magic—all gone." Even as Willow said this, her eyes betrayed her words and showed her real feelings.

Such powerful spells gone up in smoke ... a real shame.

As the book's fire smoldered out, Dawn ran over and threw her arms around her sister.

"I'm sorry, Buffy. I ... I ..."

"It's okay, Dawn. You might not believe it, but I understand."

Buffy hugged back. Then she said, "Guys, take Dawn out of here. I'll finish up."

Giles walked over to her. She looked him in the eyes and smiled, distant and bittersweet. He motioned to the group, and everyone followed him out of the abandoned hospital.

Buffy sat still for a moment and took in the silence of the place. Whenever she stopped, she could always hear the silence. Feel the emptiness.

She felt so alone.

She cried, long and hard, harder than she had in a long while. She thought of heaven, and she cried more.

Spike opened his eyes and shook his head. His whole body ached, and his vision was blurry. But his ears worked fine. He could hear Buffy's sobs close by, and he could hear her whispered words.

"I don't have anyone anymore."

He pulled himself to his feet and walked over to Buffy. He looked down at her, dusted himself off, then sat down.

"Well, you might not think much of it, but you've got me. I love you." He waited a few moments, but she didn't answer.

He moved closer. She stayed still.

He reached his hand out toward her, but stopped before they touched.

They stayed like that until she spoke.

"Spike ..."

"Yes?"

"Nevermind. It's nothing."

ABOUT THE CONTRIBUTORS

BRIAN HORTON is an artist because he enjoys telling stories with pictures. For the past five years he's had a close working relationship with Dark Horse and most notably Scott Allie as his editor. Being a fan of *Buffy*, Brian would have to say this book was a perfect project, especially collaborating with the "Dawgs." When Brian isn't making art or playing music, he shares his life with his wife Susan and dog Caldonia in Aliso Viejo, California.

JIM PASCOE lives in Los Angeles.

PAUL LEE is a painter and a freelance illustrator, who, on occasion, dabbles in comics. Paul is constantly working, which, of course, for Paul, consists mostly of lying on the floor in front of the TV and drawing, and generally making a mess at home all day. Paul's other ambition is to become a yo-yo champion and tour the country doing yo-yo tricks at local schools. Never satisfied, Paul suffers from the "grass is always greener" syndrome in which he would always rather be doing something else. Paul recently joined the Woodworker's Club and has discovered he likes power tools. Paul recommends fiber to promote regularity. He expects to win the Lotto soon, and put all this nonsense behind him.

TOM FASSBENDER, along with fellow *Creatures of Habit* scribe Jim Pascoe, writes the monthly *Buffy the Vampire Slayer* comic-book series for Dark Horse. He, too, lives in Los Angeles.

LEE, PASCOE, FASSBENDER & HORTON

Photo: AARON ODLAND

CHECK OUT THESE *BUFFY THE VAMPIRE SLAYER*™ GRAPHIC NOVELS AVAILABLE FROM COMICS SHOPS AND BOOKSTORES!

SO FEATURING FASSBENDER, SCOE, HORTON, AND LEE

**FFY THE VAMPIRE SLAYER
E BLOOD OF CARTHAGE**
den • Richards • Pimentel •
ton • Lee
or paperback
N: 1-56971-534-3 $12.95

**FFY THE VAMPIRE SLAYER
DD CHAIN**
ie • Golden • Richards •
sbender • Pascoe • Others
or paperback
N: 1-56971-602-1 $17.95

**FY THE VAMPIRE SLAYER
UMNAL**
• Fassbender • Pascoe • Richards
or paperback
N: 1-56971-554-8 $9.95

**FY THE VAMPIRE SLAYER
OF THE WOODWORK**
bender • Pascoe • Richards • Pimentel
r paperback
1: 1-56971-738-9 $12.95

**FY THE VAMPIRE SLAYER
SE MEMORIES**
bender • Pascoe • Richards • Pimentel
r paperback
1: 1-56971-736-2 $12.95

**FY THE VAMPIRE SLAYER
ATURES OF HABIT**
rated novel
bender • Pascoe • Horton • Lee
r paperback
1: 1-56971-563-7 $17.95

EL: HUNTING GROUND
en • Sniegoski • Horton • Lee • Powell
paperback
: 1-56971-547-5 $9.95

OTHER *BUFFY THE VAMPIRE SLAYER* TITLES

**BUFFY THE VAMPIRE SLAYER
THE DUST WALTZ**
Brereton • Gomez • Florea
color paperback
ISBN: 1-56971-342-1 $9.95

**BUFFY THE VAMPIRE SLAYER
THE REMAINING SUNLIGHT**
Watson • Bennett • Ketcham
color paperback
ISBN: 1-56971-354-5 $9.95

**From the original screenplay!
BUFFY THE VAMPIRE SLAYER
THE ORIGIN**
Golden • Brereton • Bennett • Ketcham
color paperback
ISBN: 1-56971-429-0 $9.95

**BUFFY THE VAMPIRE SLAYER
UNINVITED GUESTS**
Watson • Gomez • Florea
color paperback
ISBN: 1-56971-436-3 $10.95

**BUFFY THE VAMPIRE SLAYER
SUPERNATURAL DEFENSE KIT**
Watson • Richards • Pimentel
color hardcover w/slipcase comes with
golden-colored cross, "claddagh" ring,
and vial of "holy water"
ISBN: 1-56971-486-X $19.95

**BUFFY THE VAMPIRE SLAYER
BAD BLOOD**
Watson • Bennett • Ketcham
color paperback
ISBN: 1-56971-445-2 $9.95

**BUFFY THE VAMPIRE SLAYER
CRASH TEST DEMONS**
Watson • Richards • Pimentel
color paperback
ISBN: 1-56971-461-4 $9.95

**Written by *Buffy the Vampire Slayer* TV show writer Doug Petrie!
BUFFY THE VAMPIRE SLAYER
RING OF FIRE**
Petrie • Sook
color paperback
ISBN: 1-56971-482-7 $9.95

**BUFFY THE VAMPIRE SLAYER
PALE REFLECTIONS**
Watson • Richards • Pimentel
color paperback
ISBN: 1-56971-475-4 $9.95

**BUFFY THE VAMPIRE SLAYER
SPIKE AND DRU**
Marsters • Golden • Sook • Powell
color paperback
ISBN: 1-56971-541-6 $11.95

BUFFY/ANGEL: PAST LIVES
Golden • Sniegoski • Richards• Zanier
color paperback
ISBN: 1-56971-552-1 $9.95

**Written by *Buffy the Vampire Slayer* creator Joss Whedon, TV show writer Doug Petrie, Buffy's "Tara" Amber Benson, and others!
BUFFY THE VAMPIRE SLAYER
TALES OF THE SLAYERS**
Whedon • Petrie • Benson • Others
color paperback
ISBN: 1-56971-605-6 $14.95

And don't miss these *Angel* graphic novels available at comics shops & bookstores!

ANGEL: THE HOLLOWER
Golden • Gomez • Florea
color paperback
ISBN: 1-56971-450-9 $9.95

ANGEL: SURROGATES
Golden • Zanier • Owens
color paperback
ISBN: 1-56971-491-6 $9.95

ANGEL: AUTUMNAL
Golden • Sniegoski • Zanier • Powell
color paperback
ISBN: 1-56971-559-9 $9.95

ANGEL: STRANGE BEDFELLOWS
Golden • Sniegoski • Zanier • Powell
color paperback
ISBN: 1-56971-753-2 $12.95

Don't miss the ongoing adventures from *Buffy the Vampire Slayer* and *Angel* comics every month! Available at your local comics shop. To locate a comics shop in your area, call 1-888-266-4226.
www.darkhorse.com • www.buffy.com

Available from your local comics shop or bookstore!

To find a comics shop in your area, call 1-888-266-4226
For more information or to order direct:
•On the web: www.darkhorse.com •E-mail: mailorder@darkhorse.com
•Phone: 1-800-862-0052 or (503) 652-9701 Mon.-Sat. 9 A.M. to 5 P.M. Pacific Time
*Prices and availability subject to change without notice

STAKE OUT THESE BUFFY THE VAMPIRE SLAYER AND ANGEL TRADE PAPERBACKS

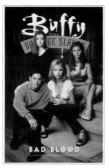